The
Second
Career

Wilder Penfield, O.M., M.D., F.R.S.

The
Second
Career

WITH OTHER ESSAYS AND ADDRESSES

LITTLE, BROWN AND COMPANY / BOSTON — TORONTO

CONTENTS

DEDICATED TO *Sir William Osler*, M.D., F.R.S.

Preface

This book is intended for popular reading. The addresses and essays I have selected for it were written during a career in neurosurgery, or shortly after. But they are more directly concerned with education, history, and the philosophy of life than they are with medicine and science. Nearly all were prepared, originally, in response to outside requests, and such requests often proved useful since they compelled me to state and to elaborate what I hoped would be of value to others.

In a way it is true of every man – or it should be true – that his second career begins as soon as he embarks on the primary job that will yield him a livelihood. Whatever he does as citizen or parent is part of the second career, and the two run concurrently until perhaps the second outlasts the first. Thus these essays, written in hours of professional idling and now adapted to form a book, are products of my own second career. "The Approach to Authorship" (No. 4) was begun in the hope of seeing clearly the differences between scientific writing and creative authorship. It describes the adventures of one who is still trying to cross the intervening country.

Higher education is a legitimate subject of interest for any professional specialist. My thoughts on it were initially expressed, in a rather flippant mood, at Princeton in 1937 (No. 2, "The Alumnus Phenomenon"). A somewhat more sober approach (No. 3) was made at the University of British Columbia in 1960.

In a few of the addresses, scientific information was presented to a lay audience – always a difficult task. To avoid misconception on the part of hearers or readers, the scientific worker must learn new ways of expression, and in the process he may well discover some practical applications to which he was blind before.

Essay Number 12, "The Neurophysiology of Speech and Some Educational Consequences", was read to the American Academy of Arts and Sciences as the address expected from a new member. It brought me quite naturally to an active interest in the field of multilingual education and led to other addresses such as the one that follows it in this book.

"The Physiological Basis of the Mind" (No. 14) was part of a University of California symposium. This was a still more difficult matter to explain because our knowledge of the mechanisms involved is so incomplete. But it seemed worth the effort in view of its importance to an understanding of Man and Civilization, the subject of the symposium. I had made an attempt at it years before in a broadcast, as part of a British Broadcasting Corporation symposium. I had tried again, hoping to do a better job, in an address to the American Philosophical Society where it is the custom for members to speak in simple terms on subjects which would, without considerable effort, appear most complicated.

But this is preamble enough. If any quotation were to be used as a foreword to the book, the words of Job, from which the title of one address was taken, would serve the purpose for all: "But where shall wisdom be found? and where is the place of understanding?"

We are moulded to some extent by the heroes we choose as companions to go with us through life. No disciple can borrow greatness; he can only use such wit as he has, in an ever-changing world. But he may adopt the manner of work and the way of life he has admired. The reader will easily recognize my own heroes, for they come and go across the pages of the book. There is one companion whose influence may not be so obvious. My wife has listened to all these writings with patience, and has criticized with wise understanding. If there is virtue here, much of it comes from her. To my friend and secretary, Anne Dawson, special thanks are due for constructive help in preparing the material.

WILDER PENFIELD

The Second Career

The days of our years are
three score years and ten;
and if by reason of strength
they be fourscore years,
yet is their strength
labour and sorrow.

The psalmist, David, who wrote those words lived three thousand years ago, and yet in his pastoral surroundings he expected to live as long as we do today: seventy years, or, by reason of strength, eighty years, or even by chance, one hundred years. His expectation was fulfilled, for he was thirty years a shepherd and soldier, and forty years ruler of Israel. David had time for a second career, and that brings me to the subject of this essay.

It would seem that modern science has not really changed man's normal span of life. Nineteen hundred years ago, Pliny the Elder wrote that centenarians were common enough at that time in Rome. He even told of an actress who boasted that she had survived a hundred years. The change which we should recognize in this generation is that more men and women reach life's true goal, fulfilling the cycle set for us, bypassing the plagues and disease and famine.

Our population increase is not all due to the high birth-rate and low infant-mortality rate. There is also a sharp rise in the proportion of men over sixty. This might mean an added burden on society unless some thought is given to the matter. It is

AN ADDRESS TO THE CANADIAN CLUB OF MONTREAL, DECEMBER 1959.

difficult to say how the accepted rules of retirement were established. But it is likely that they were influenced in no small measure by William Osler.

Osler? Who was he? Outside of the medical profession today, many may never have heard of him. They were born too late to remember the angry outburst that filled the newspapers fifty-five years ago after his retirement address. "MEN USELESS AFTER FORTY," the newspaper headlines screamed. "SHOULD BE CHLOROFORMED AT SIXTY." Osler had joked once too often. He had overstated his true belief. That is all forgotten now. But forgotten rumours – true and false alike – sometimes live on, indestructible, to shape the thinking of a later day.

William Osler was born in 1849 at Bond Head, a village in Upper Canada, later called Ontario. After his education in Toronto, Montreal, and abroad, he became Professor of Medicine at four universities in brilliant succession. His age when working in each institution is significant: McGill – age 25 to 35; the University of Pennsylvania – 35 to 40; Johns Hopkins – 40 to 56; Oxford – 56 to 70. At seventy he died.

On leaving Baltimore to go to Oxford, he delivered his farewell address with, as he said, "mingled feelings of gratitude and sorrow." He realized quite well that retirement from Johns Hopkins meant retirement from his active life, because medical courses at Oxford at that time embraced only pre-clinical subjects, and he was a clinical physician.

There is inevitably a mood of melancholy that comes to any man on retirement. While preparing this address, Osler must have been in such a mood. To escape interruption, he slipped away from Baltimore and took the train for New York to finish it in the library of the University Club there. He called his address "The Fixed Period", taking the name from Anthony Trollope's fanciful novel about a college of men who agreed that each of them would be chloroformed on reaching the age of sixty.

"I have two fixed ideas," he said at the farewell dinner. "The first is the comparative uselessness of men above forty years of age ... My second fixed idea is the uselessness of men above sixty years of age, and the incalculable benefit it would be in commercial, political and in professional life if, as a matter of course, men stopped work at this age."

Then with tongue in cheek, and probably feeling safe from misunderstanding because of his own age, he continued as follows: "As it can be maintained that all the great advances have come from men under forty, so the history of the world shows that a very large proportion of the evils may be traced to the sexagenarians . . . all of the worst poems, most of the bad pictures, a majority of the bad novels, not a few of the bad sermons and, I hesitate to add, speeches."

The news-gatherers of the public press in the United States were bored at the time, for lack of sensational news. They pounced on Osler's words with glee. Here, they reported, was the cold and calculated opinion of a scientist, the most distinguished physician in the English-speaking world. The story flashed around the globe.

After the storm had struck, Osler tried to point out that a part of his talk was "pleasantry." But, alas, it was too late. Anger and astonishment swept the country. Men talked with horror of "Oslerizing" the aged. In St. Louis a man of sixty killed himself, leaving an empty chloroform bottle on the bed beside him, together with clippings from the address.

Not all newspapers took Osler so seriously. On the second day of the furore, the Montreal *Gazette* published a delightfully understanding quotation from the London *Telegraph* of the day before: "Dr. Osler is to be congratulated on the success of his little jest. He will add to the gaiety of Oxford, if he can stir it to depths by similar playfulness. It is no small feat to have deluded into seriousness a nation of humorists."

Osler was distressed, but he made no further public statements. However, almost two years later, the Regius Professor of Medicine at Oxford, now Sir William, included that same address, "The Fixed Period", unchanged in a second edition of his collected addresses entitled *Aequanimitas*. In the Preface he referred to the intended joke about chloroform thus:

"To every man over sixty whose spirit I may have unwittingly bruised, I tender my heartfelt regrets. Let me add, however, that the discussion which followed my remarks has not changed, but has rather strengthened, my belief that the real work of life is done before the fortieth year and that after the sixtieth year it would be best for the world and best for themselves if men rested from their labours."

This, then, was his final opinion. What should ours be, more than half a century later? The answer, it seems to me, may be found in a reconsideration of Osler's own career. Instead of disappearing into retirement when he sailed for Oxford, content, as he had said, to "rest from his labours," he actually embarked on a second career as a scholar.

He fitted into Oxford life easily, gracefully. There was time for classical study, writing, and book-collecting. But his career as a teacher and practitioner of medicine had come to an end. He carried out no further basic or clinical research. And yet his influence on the world of medicine did not grow less. It was true, of course, that he had been developing his talents in the field of scholarship secondarily during the ten years of his basic study and investigation at the Montreal General Hospital, and during the twenty-one years of his teaching and clinic-organization in the United States.

The impact of this second career may be discovered in the Osler biography which was published in 1925, six years after his death. It was written by the neurosurgeon, Harvey Cushing, then Professor of Surgery at Harvard. Cushing had come under the spell of Osler at an earlier period when they were both in Baltimore. Volume I of the biography deals with the first fifty-six years of Osler's life; the second is concerned only with the fourteen years that remained to him after he went to Oxford. And yet there are 685 pages in Volume I and 686 pages (not counting the index) in Volume II. If Osler had died when he retired from Johns Hopkins, one half of the things his biographer considered of interest to posterity would have been lost. And it may be added that Cushing's life of Sir William Osler won the Pulitzer Prize for Biography in 1926.

It may well be true, as Osler urged in his farewell address, that "the effective, moving, vitalizing work of the world is done between the ages of twenty-five and forty." That is a matter of opinion, but this, it seems to me, is certain: every year from birth to death has its purpose and should have its use. Understanding is born from the hard work and experience of early life. Understanding grows with the years, and with it perspective and wisdom. There is no limit to the uses of these things this side of the grave, and we would do well to make them available to society today.

Scientific advance has presented society with many embarrassing dilemmas. But it is useless to turn out the electric light, or to bring back the trotting horse. We must learn to control our destiny by a corresponding achievement in moral and political fields. It is the vigorous and potentially productive individuals among our senior citizens that I would discuss, not those who are ill or senile. Hospitals, old people's homes and old age pensions have served a useful purpose in the past. But no government, however welfare-minded, should hope to solve an employment problem by building rest homes for able-bodied men who are not ready for rest and do not want to rust out the remainder of their lives.

The theory that the man or woman of sixty has nothing more to contribute to society, during the ten or twenty years of active life that remain, is wrong. The belief that men in later years cannot learn new skills, and educated men new professions, is false. Most men who retire could, and would, continue in constructive work if they saw that they were needed. But many of them face a paralysing psychological misconception. They are halted by it, although there is often no true physical or mental disability. Let me describe to you the evolution of a little-recognized disease. It is a psychological malady which we might name *pseudo-senility* or *false senility*.

A worthy citizen employed in business, for example, or in industry or education or government, reaches his time of statutory retirement. Some colleague, who happens to have a larger bank account of unspent years, comes to him and gives him a gold watch and tells him to take a well- earned rest. That man, who yesterday was busy and capable of contributing something that was of value, now stays home. He mows the lawn and carries out the garbage for his wife while he thinks about his future. When he is well-behaved she lets him wash the dishes. He notices that his recent memory is not as good as it was when he was younger, although distant memory is good enough. He doesn't know that this is caused by the fact that the hippocampal gyrus in the temporal lobe of each side of the brain often suffers some interference in its circulation, while the rest of the brain is as good as ever for many years to come.

Perhaps, then, some friend who is well-meaning but devoid of a sense of humour (most people have at least one such friend) comes to comfort him. "Enjoy yourself," he says; "that is all that remains for you to do. Just have a good time." Then, in a little while, people begin to say, behind his back of course: "He is going to pieces, poor fellow." And so he is, fast.

He thinks he is good for nothing, not realizing that people who are good for nothing don't think so. He begins to disintegrate. The only thing that could be guaranteed to make him disintegrate faster would be an increased intake of alcohol. That man is suffering from a delusion of incompetence, not from incompetence itself; a retirement neurosis of *false senility*.

The whole trouble was that what he needed when he was given the gold watch was a new job, a difficult job – not a rest. Beyond the normal rhythm of work and sleep, rest was not what he needed. Rest, with nothing else, results in rust. It corrodes the mechanisms of the brain. The rhubarb that no one picks goes to seed.

Now, it is a curious fact that women rarely suffer from the neurosis of *false senility*. Perhaps it is because they are less easily deluded! But I suspect that it is because most women have a second career that no one needs to plan. When they have raised a family, or finished a profession, or when they have finished with both, they turn to full-time housekeeping. And no prudent man would dare to say that this is not essential and important.

The time of retirement should be reorganized and renamed. It is the time for embarking on a new career, the last career perhaps, but not necessarily a less enjoyable one; not, perhaps, a less useful one to society. Disease and disability may overtake men at any age, of course, and force them to withdraw from work. But the capacity of the human brain for certain purposes often increases right through the years that are marked for standard retirement. And who can say? – those purposes may be what the world today needs most.

I do not urge that the time for a man to retire from his

primary career should be postponed – not at all. A second career can quite well begin by the age of sixty. It should start by then at the latest, even if formal retirement takes place at sixty-five or later. His preparation for a second career should be undertaken long before that, preferably in the forties. Better yet that it should come with him from school days.

When a man reaches his sixties, he should be released from heavy harness, but he should be given the opportunity of starting on a new or modified career. The nature of that career must depend on interest and ability. It should provide greater latitude of living, allow a variable or decreasing amount of physical labour.

Here is a problem for executives, statesmen and educators. They may well discover that this growing army of senior citizens need be no added load to society; quite the contrary. They must, however, provide a stage of transition and perhaps courses of preparation. There is an ancient adage that you cannot teach an old dog new tricks. That adage is not true, not for men, and not for dogs either. It is also not true that men have no contribution to make in the last twenty or thirty years of life.

No one can deny that the human brain passes through certain inexorable changes. Senescence will come in time, inevitably. The brain has a specialized capacity for the beginning of languages during the first decade of life. After that time it is ready for expansion of vocabulary. It is ready for mathematics, rationalization, independent thought. At sixty the body has certainly passed beyond its greatest strength, and physical demands should be lessened and changed. But the brain, quite often, is ready for its best performance in certain fields.

New jobs call for the use of previously unused nerve-cell connections in the brain. This is perfectly possible in the sixties. The "old dog" will increase his previous capacity by taking on a challenging new job. Consider soldiers like Eisenhower and De Gaulle, who were pushed into second careers as statesmen. Challenge calls forth unsuspected greatness in the common man, and in the uncommon. Consider Clemenceau, Adenauer and Voltaire in their eighties; Verdi composing his greatest operas between seventy-four and eighty; Michelangelo painting the Last Judgment at sixty. Look at Winston Churchill! When he had reached the age of seventy-nine he was too busy to go to Stockholm to accept the Nobel Prize for work in the field of his second career, that of literature. His wife had to pick up the Prize for him as though it were a notice from the post office.

A genius is not a man who was made in some other image; he is just a man driven to constructive action by a great enthusiasm. Enthusiasm feeds on challenge. The ordinary brain is good enough for most men and most purposes. Its best tonic is use; the worst treatment is discouragement and disuse.

Herein lies a great educational opportunity – the training of retiring men for second careers. Not everyone will be ready to decide for himself what his second career might be. Corporations and colleges and governments may have to put the man who is approaching the statutory age-limit through a set of psychological tests. This will call for new techniques of testing. Those who can pass should be entitled to training for new jobs, honourable ones.

Critical exploration of this field will discover, I suspect, that a broad early education serves the specialist best. All men become specialists in time if they accomplish anything. A second career means a change in a man's specialization. The breadth of education which makes this change easy is to be acquired outside the school more often, perhaps, than in it; acquired by independent study, hobbies, reading, travel, curiosity. Thus the windows of the mind may be opened to many varied fields of knowledge and endeavour.

Let us reconsider the closing years of man, the knowing animal, *homo sapiens*, who knows so much about his world, so little about himself.

The length of man's allotted life on earth is seventy years, or by reason of strength, eighty, ninety or a hundred. The miracle of birth begins his day, and death is the end. Immortality may be his hope, but not immortality here in this body. In our turbulent world, love and kindliness are man's most welcome blessings; work to good purpose his most treasured privilege.

Toward the end, senescence with its comforting drowsiness closes stealthily one door after another. And so when death does come at last, it may not be unwelcome after all. Science has not changed these things. The span of life, for those who escape its early perils, is about the same today as when David played on his harp before King Saul.

To most men, there should come a time for shifting harness, for lightening the load one way and adjusting it for greater effort in another. That is the time for the second career, time for the old dog to perform new tricks. The new career may bring in little or no money; it may be concerned only with good works. It may, on the other hand, bring in support that is much needed. It can be a delight to a man, who comes at last to a well-earned job instead of a well-earned rest. It can be, too, what society needs most from him.

The problem to set before the wise men of today is simply this: How can each individual be given the chance to work? Sometimes the race is not to the swift nor the battle to the strong. It may be that the last work of the old man's hands will serve society best – and him as well.

The Alumnus Phenomenon

[TWO]

What is the good of an "old Grad"? I asked myself that question twenty-odd years ago when, for the first time, I saw groups of quaintly dressed adults capering across the campus. Late that night I was awakened by one of them bellowing into my room. Being a crude undergraduate, my first instinct was to obliterate the source of the bellow. But a certain unreasoned reverence for senility stayed my hand and I dropped to sleep, eventually, pondering the problem – what is the good of an "old Grad" to Princeton?

Graduates like ourselves, with assumed privileges and with real loyalty to an *alma mater*, constitute a new and interesting phenomenon, developed recently in the United States and Canada. Even the word *alumnus*, meaning foster-child, is heard only on this side of the water.

It has been said that the function of a university is to bring face to face teacher and teacher, teacher and student, and student and student. These relationships have long been primary considerations but our relationship to the university from which we graduated is a very much later afterthought. Our role, however, was discharged from early times by other agencies and I shall present an historical explanation, possibly a justification, of the alumnus.

A sudden widespread demand for scholarly teaching brought universities into existence in the Middle Ages. Our forbears from northern Europe had previously overturned the reservoirs of Grecian and Roman learning and lost it all, as it seemed

THE ALUMNI DAY ADDRESS, PRINCETON UNIVERSITY; FEBRUARY, 1937.

irretrievably, but a small trickle of scholarship continued within the Church and even bubbled up occasionally in a secret well in some unsuspected monastery.

In the eighth century, we find Charles the Great laboriously trying to learn to read and write after he had conquered the world. He realized very well how slender was the store of knowledge in his day, for he said to his teacher, Alcuin, that he longed to have in his kingdom twelve clergy as learned as Jerome or Augustine. Alcuin, shocked at such an immoderate demand, replied: "The Lord of Heaven and Earth had but two such, and thou wouldst have twelve?" What Charles really wanted in place of his palace school was a university. What would he have said could he have envisioned the combined knowledge of the 338 members of Princeton's faculty; what if he had been able to contrast with this the total knowledge remaining from their teaching in the heads of Princeton's thirteen thousand graduates!

In the twelfth century the hidden streams of scholarship came to the surface and swelled into a great current that swept through the towns of Europe. In Bologna, student guilds or universities formed a permanent organization; in Paris a guild of masters did the same; and toward the end of the century a university began to emerge from the mists of the Thames valley at Oxford. For a long time Oxford refused this secondary historical position and claimed origin from the time of good King Mempric, supposed to have ruled in Britain when Saul reigned in Judea. But their bluff has been called, for even Mempric proved to be only a myth and Oxford really first appeared in the reign of Edward II, who seems to have shared with Charlemagne an urge for adult education.

Those were days when students were men (if not always scholars). How different from the anaemic youths of today! At Bologna the undergraduates ranged in age from seventeen to forty years. They came from all the awakened world, filled with a longing to learn and also to fight. They formed their own guilds or universities which gave them rights of citizenship in that foreign city.

A professor was any man whom these independent gentlemen would hire to teach them. The professors also formed guilds, called colleges. A struggle ensued but the students quite properly subdued the masters to an incredible servitude. The masters retained one right only and that was to judge who had passed his examinations so as to be admitted to the profession of law (for Bologna arose as a centre for the study of Roman law). The masters did issue a few disregarded statutes, such as that scholars should sit "as quietly as girls" and should not shout during lectures. In the fifteenth century at Leipzig, masters even ventured so far as to set down the following energetic list of penalties:

1. *Fine of ten new groschen for lifting a stone or other missile with a view to throwing it at a master but not actually throwing.*
2. *For throwing and missing, eight florins.*
3. *For wounding without mutilating, eighteen florins and compensation to master.*
4. *For actual mutilation, expulsion.*

Evidently by the fifteenth century it was concluded that in case a difference of opinion between student and master led to such damage to the person of the master as to make him useless for further teaching, the student should in all fairness go elsewhere. It was apparently not necessary to protect the student.

The power of the undergraduates lay in their ability to boycott professors, tradesmen, and even cities. For example, on one occasion the beautiful daughter of a rich Bolognese citizen was abducted by a scholar. The city thereupon meted out the punishment of death to the young man. The student guild was called together and decided the city had treated a trifling matter much too seriously. Consequently the whole university migrated to Siena, taking with them many of their professors.

There is actually a record of such a migration of two thousand students from Prague to Oxford on one occasion, but even if it were only two hundred it seems an amazing feat today. We must remember, however, that there was no language barrier as all teaching was carried out in Latin, and a scholar had to speak Latin and at least pretend to understand it before entering any university.

In university squabbles the Pope usually gave his powerful support to the students, and it was from the Pope that the universities of both Paris and Oxford eventually secured the first recognition of their corporate existence. The intervention of the Church as a university ally is important. It brings on to the stage, so busily occupied by pupil and master, an outside actor. It may seem a very far cry from the Vatican to a reunion tent, but this is a foreshadowing of the alumnus in history.

Oxford began her chartered history with an incident similar to the one described above concerning Bologna. An undergraduate killed a woman at Maiden Hall, a building since replaced by New College, no doubt wisely. The young man fled. The mayor and townsmen arrested two or three innocent fellow-clerks from his lodging and with the easy permission of King John had them hanged. As a result of this incident masters and scholars fled in various directions, some, it is said, to Cambridge where they helped to bring into the world another university. The Pope espoused the cause of the scattered students and there ensued a struggle between him and King John in which the king was eventually defeated. The fugitives returned triumphant after the city fathers had walked barefoot into each of Oxford's churches seeking forgiveness and chanting a psalm of repentance.

This is all very interesting perhaps, but the important fact is that the first university subsidy resulted from the hanging of those innocent undergraduates. The Legatine Ordinance which settled this affair instructed the city of Oxford to pay in the year 1214 and thereafter for eternity an annual sum of fifty-two shillings which was to be used for poor students, and to give them a feast on St. Nicholas's Day. Today this payment is still made annually by the Crown, although the sum has unaccountably grown to 61s. 6d.

The downfall of the student really began at Paris and Oxford where the masters' guilds had had the upper hand from the start. The scholars were young, from thirteen to twenty years as an average age; and in the sixteenth century, even flogging reared its ugly head in the universities.

At this time Oxford was in the habit of granting to pre-university teachers a degree called "Master in Grammar." At his inception the master was given, instead of the usual book, two academic symbols of his profession: a "palmer" and a "birch." He thereupon began his career at once by flogging a boy who was ready at hand "openlye in the Scolys." He then paid the bedel one groat for the birch and the same to the boy "for hys labour."

In Paris, where fees were demanded by the masters for all favours to students, the jovial custom grew up of "drinking the surplus" at some neighbouring tavern, a duty discharged uncomplainingly by the masters alone. The final triumph of the don occurred, however, at Oxford and Cambridge where the colleges walled in their wild students and separated the town from the gown by many rules and regulations. When the senior students of Merton College elected a new warden they were closeted and starved into unanimity of opinion by a "subtraction of victuals."

The College of New Jersey first gasped for the breath of enlightenment in 1747. Struggling to its feet, it seems to have tottered as far as Newark and from there it shortly found its way to a hilltop in Princeton. But the beginning of our university, like all universities of today, goes back to Salerno, Bologna, and Paris. In Princeton the Presbyterian Synod planted something they thought was derived from the British Isles, but something unpremeditated resulted.

The following lines of Stephen Benét illustrate this strange germination:

> *They tried to fit you with an English song*
> *And clip your speech into an English tale.*
> *But even from the first, the words went wrong,*
> *The catbird pecked away the nightingale.*
> *The homesick men begot high-cheekboned things*
> *Whose wit was whittled with a different sound*
> *And Thames and all the rivers of the kings*
> *Ran into Mississippi and were drowned.*
> *They planted England with a stubborn trust,*
> *But the cleft dust was never English dust.*

And now, eight centuries after Bologna, what do we find today in universities such as Princeton? A disciplined body of students who dig obediently in subterranean libraries where they bury their love of learning and seem to lose it – for when they emerge to the open air, academic discussion is "bad form." A startling change! The old love of fighting still exists, but it has been cleverly diverted into athletics and extracurricular activities.

The masters seem to have won the day. In addition to graduating whom they like they can now admit whom they choose and teach him what they think best in whatever manner they please. Ask in full meeting of the faculty whether they need help in determining academic policy. I suspect that at all events they will not call for help from us who yesterday heard them so credulously.

Thus the University is carrying out its function of bringing together, first, master and student – presumably to the benefit of both, but certainly to the benefit of the master; secondly, master and master – the benefit is evidenced by modern research, and in some institutions, like the one chaperoned by Dr. Flexner, the Institute for Advanced Study, the masters have such pleasure in each other that students have almost been forgotten; thirdly, student with student – a contact which is now a great force, for undergraduate life has become a microcosm which moulds its victims into one rigid form, the college man – a worthy person, no doubt, but sadly uninteresting.

What then is our function? We are not continuing scholars. We no longer discuss the subjects of the classroom. Alas! we never did. I hope at least that we may dissociate ourselves from those "old Grads" who bellow into dormitory rooms at reunions. They might be considered to form a separate body called Continuing Undergraduates, strange examples of arrested development, physiologically interesting but socially stupid. We have become business men, professional men, fathers – with a special interest in and love for this spirit of Princeton, a spirit which I cannot describe but which I seem to recognize more clearly in the undergraduates and graduates than I do in the faculty. Spiritually, therefore, we would seem to be a part of this university.

If we organize at all we do so freely, not to repay a debt; but once organized our only formal relationship to the University is a financial one. From the beginning, the Pope protected and the Church supported universities. Wealthy churchmen and kings endowed the English colleges, and governmental and civil agencies have done the same on the Continent. Princeton has neither church nor king to support her and the government of the State of New Jersey is strangely silent in matters financial. Here, then, as a body we have a grave responsibility.

Have we also the right to interfere with Princeton's policies? No. I am afraid it is quite useless for us to try. Our predecessors, Pope and Prince, tried and failed ignominiously. Have we the right to criticize? Yes; no one can stop us. We may reasonably demand to know why there is so much university teaching and so little education; so many years of learning, so scanty a harvest of culture. Abraham Flexner has accused the American university of too great expansion, of allowing trade and commerce to enter the halls of arts and sciences. The accusation is true, although Princeton has sinned less in this regard than many universities.

But there is something more important than what is taught, and that is the manner of teaching. Chemistry taught in a scholarly manner has more humanizing value than a sterile course in philosophy, and an essay on vitamins gives just as much opportunity for training in English as one on Shakespeare. It is our right to demand a scholarly training for Princeton undergraduates, but nothing more.

We have no right to expect any university to provide culture of itself. Culture is a by-product of living. It is usually acquired, if acquired at all, at home. There are elements of training, of breeding, of inheritance in it. School and college may contribute but they alone cannot recapture the indefinable thing which some of our ancestors brought to this continent. Pioneers as they were, they poured it out in the wilderness and their sons lost it, preoccupied with the problem of survival.

The second task of the alumnus, therefore, is to play his part in the elaboration of a new culture in the homes of a new land. What was learned in the "four long years of college" may perhaps prove useful to those who face that task seriously.

But it is we who are responsible for the culture, or the lack of it, in our sons and their sons, not Princeton.

The university, if it has a collective consciousness, must look upon this alumnus organization as a strange new phenomenon, a neoplasm, an unexpected somatic excrescence. She must regard what I have called the Continuing Undergraduate with alarm. But the whole situation is of her own making. No doubt she might have done a better job, but there are human failings for which there is no cure, even in a university; which reminds me of a poem written in Sanskrit centuries before Christ and long, long before the university had reared its head. Ryder's translation is as follows:

> *A fire with water we defeat,*
> *With parasols the midday heat,*
> *Mad elephants with goads that prick,*
> *Oxen and asses with a stick . . .*
> *Science has cures for every ill*
> *Except the fool; he prospers still.*

The university is in some ways the most durable structure in modern society, aloof from religious differences and superior to war and political upheaval, which may shake but which cannot destroy her. An incurable beggar but stronger than all her patrons, the university converts her resources into the scholarly hope of enlightenment, without which these modern times would indeed be depressing.

Princeton has need of the help of her alumni, help which she can secure neither from church nor state, and she can give you in return for your generosity and your constructive criticism a hope for the salvation of society which you might otherwise seek in vain.

To Cultivate the Groves of Academus

[THREE]

In the City of Athens, if you pass along the highway that leads out toward the laurel grove where Greeks celebrate the national wine festival, you will come to a block in the traffic. An ancient olive tree stands in a little patch of earth in the centre of the street, and crowding men and donkeys turn aside to pass around it, like a rushing stream around a stone. Trucks halt and truckers honk impatiently. If it is spring and the festival is on, the crowding is worse, and resentful faces peer out at the tree from sleek limousines on their way to the tasting of the wine.

The gigantic trunk is no more than a hollow shell, but lusty daughters are growing from its roots and grey-green olive leaves ripple along their branches, fresh and new like the leaves of the parent tree when it was young, 2,300 years ago. This, Athenians say, is the sole survivor of the olive trees in the famous Grove of Academus. This tree stood outside the walls of Athens on the banks of a now-vanished stream called Cephissus. Here it was that Plato walked with his disciples and talked of abstract ideas, morals and mathematics.

That talk still echoes in the academic halls of our colleges today. Our students wear the cap and gown derived no doubt from the elegant cap and short cloak that Plato's pupils wore. This, the uniform of higher learning, was even then the target of jests from the townsmen. Only the term "egg-head" was left to the inspiration of a modern "nitwit" in the twentieth century.

I would like to look at the Grove of Academus and then

THE YORK LECTURE, UNIVERSITY OF BRITISH COLUMBIA; VANCOUVER, OCTOBER 1960.

consider the problem of how to cultivate the academic groves around the world today. But first, a word about Plato. This, as everyone knows, was a nickname given to the aristocratic young Athenian. He was called by his parents Aristocles but was commonly known as Platon, from *platus*, meaning broad. The word doubtless described his neck and shoulders, for he had been a wrestler in the Isthmian games. These were famous pan-Hellenic athletic competitions held in Corinth. They were second only to the Olympic games, in the eyes of the citizens of greater Hellas.

This broad-shouldered young man was handsome, popular and versatile. He was said to delight in Euripides, in athletics and in the admiration of women. When he reached the age of twenty he was apparently undecided whether to choose a career in poetry or one in politics. But he abandoned such ideas when Socrates, that strange, ugly philosopher, came his way and he fell under the Socratic spell.

Socrates was a teacher who had no academy, no place to teach. Instead, he walked to and fro in the agora of Athens, inquiring into the minds of men, probing their motives, seeking to define the good, to discover a soul, to put into words some concept of ethical behaviour. The material for his study was to be found in men's minds. He searched for a spirit beyond the mind of the individual and a spirit, too, beyond the several gods of Mount Olympus. He seemed to perceive the presence of a being behind the gods of Greece who was not so different from the conception of God in the minds of men today.

When Plato met Socrates, he burned his own poems and joined the followers of this new master. He went about with him, making notes of his conversations, until that dramatic day when the citizens of Athens could stand the recurring sting of the "gadfly" no longer, and Socrates was called upon to drink the poison hemlock.

That was in the year 399 B.C. when the disciple Plato was probably twenty-eight years of age. He saw that his carefree confident youth was at an end, and he left Athens in despair and anger. Thirteen years followed during which he wandered about, to live in many cities and to study in the mathematical school of the Pythagoreans. He served as a soldier, too, and finally he was captured and sold into slavery. His friends in Athens heard of it and ransomed him. So he came back home at the age of forty-one.

On his arrival there, the man who had paid for his ransom, Anniceris by name, refused to accept from Plato's other friends the sums that they had raised. Consequently three thousand drachmas were left over. They converted that into the first recorded academic endowment! It was invested in the olive grove, on the banks of the Cephissus, which was called the Grove of Academus. This became Plato's home and when pupils came to him from the city, it was soon converted to an institution of higher learning. In time, it was called *Academia* according to Plutarch who quoted a contemporary description as follows: "A beautiful, well-watered garden where philosophers meet and express their irreligious views on the nature of the gods." Obviously, *Academia* had its adverse critics. But it also had its ardent supporters since it continued as an intellectual centre for nine centuries.

In Plato's lifetime there were numerous gifts and endowments, directed to the teacher since Plato, unlike other philosophers throughout Greece, charged no fee to his disciples. Suidas stated that "from time to time [rich men] bequeathed in their wills, to members of the school, the means of living a life of philosophic leisure." Obviously these served as continuing fellowships. Diogenes Laertius states that the tyrant Dionysius II was said to have given Plato the unbelievable sum of eighty talents, about $480,000. "This," Will Durant has pointed out dryly, "might explain the philosopher's patience with the King."

There is no record of what the requirements for admission to *Academia* may have been, but at least we know that there was an inscription over the entrance that read *medeis ageometretos eisito,* which might be translated "Let no one enter here without geometry."*

I have asked you to look back with me across the whole history of academic institutions to the first one; back to the Grove of Academus. What was going on in that grove was also going on

---

* Will Durant, *The Life of Greece.* New York: Simon & Schuster, Inc., 1939.

elsewhere in ancient Greece, and had been for a century or more. Here a poet, there an astronomer or a mathematician, musician, sculptor, painter, philosopher, orator, historian, trage-dian, emerged from the ranks of educated citizens. Soon disciples came to him to listen and learn and to strike out for themselves, or to turn to other teachers.

It was the random blossoming of genius as though in a garden whose fateful seeding had been kept a secret from those whose task it was to tend it. The soil in which such varied genius germinated was Greek education. That system of ed-ucation was common throughout greater Greece, which was made up of many city-states, some ruled by tyrants but more of them by democractic election. In spite of the independence of so many states, the people were not divided. They had a common literature, and a common religion and folk-lore. Greek religion differed from all others in this: There was no prohib-ition against new thinking. The gods, like the Greeks them-selves, seemed to consider freedom essential and natural.

For a long time, strange to say, the only formal bond of union between these independent cities was the pan-Hellenic league of sports. From the days when the people first appeared in history while conquering and settling the shores of the Eastern Mediterranean, on down to the culmination of their civilization, they took delight in athletic games conducted always before a temple of a Greek god.

Athletic festivals soon came to include contests of the mind as well as of the body. Greek contestants, naturally, sought to outstrip their opponents, but there was an aim, beyond that, for which we have no word today. It consisted in the production of a supreme performance, carried out perhaps in an agony of effort. They called this *aretê*. It has been translated "virtue" from the writings of Plato. Virtue, however, has in it an element of goodness that is not included in *aretê*, and it lacks the sense of effort and agony which *aretê* includes. *Aretê*, Greeks believed, was what pleased the god before whom the games were held. It brought admiration from other Greeks. Kitto* has described this essential national ideal as "outstanding excellence..."

---

* H. D. F. Kitto, *The Greeks*, 1951. Penguin Books Ltd.

"It was *aretê*," he said, "that the games were designed to test – the *aretê* of the whole man, not merely a specialized skill." This outstanding excellence was what the Greek student, teacher, artist and thinker was expected to set up for himself as his own personal aim.

In recent years the great nations have discovered with apparent surprise that intellectual leadership is the goal, the prize above all else, to be sought in world-wide competition. Defence, perhaps survival, may depend on superiority of the mind, and not on the circumference of a leader's arm as in times gone by.

Today, governments are turning, bewildered and perhaps not quite convinced, to their own academic institutions, hopefully demanding much. But excellence does not come to command, nor genius either. Little added speed can be forced from a long-starved horse by shouts or the use of a whip.

Those of us who watch today from the Groves of Academus see a world in rapid change. New nations, struggling to their feet, look about for guidance. Men who have little of this world's goods are demanding more in what Dean Rusk has aptly termed the "revolution of rising expectations." Across the world we see the mounting tides of population that will bring the nations to a famine unless the birth-rate is reduced.

We watch the giants struggle for their ideologies in which the brotherhood of man has been forgotten – communist dictatorships striving to expand, capitalist freedoms in confused opposition. We see the gathering clouds of fear and suspicion and hear the rumbling thunder of atomic threats.

Ministers of Defence may turn to the universities, demanding more physicists and more chemists. But what the people of the world want, and need, is leadership of mind and spirit. They want to find the path toward kindness and the brotherhood of man, and peace. And where can it be found if not in the institutions that have sought the truth since the days of Socrates and Plato? The cure for our problems is probably not to be discovered by physicist or chemist. But no one can predict in what soil genius will flower, nor can the nature of its flowering be predetermined.

Here is our problem: how can we bring forth genius as the Greeks did? If it will not come to command, can it be bought?

The answer to this, it seems to me, is "yes," but only if accompanied by certain changes in society.

Most scholars will agree that the intellectual contribution of Greece in classical times was unique. Such a thing has only happened once in the whole history of mankind. How could the Greeks, who were neither numerous nor wealthy, achieve so much? Was the Greek type an evolutionary variant? Did he have better muscles, stronger bones and a superior brain?

I believe the answer to that must be "no." Since history began, there has been no definite evidence of further structural improvement in the brain of man. The Greeks did not discover writing for themselves, nor how to sail a ship. When they migrated from an unknown region of northern Europe to Crete and the coasts of the eastern Mediterranean, they were taught these things and much else by the people they conquered. Their alphabet came from the Phoenicians, and doubtless their seamanship. The kindred people that they left behind were not outstanding, nor are their own descendants, living on in Greece today. The secret of Greek genius must be found in the conditions of Greek life between the sixth and third centuries B.C. It must lie in the background of Greek education as it developed in the cities of the Aegean.

During the dark ages, the Greeks were nearly forgotten. Then the mediaeval universities came into being, and Greek and Latin scholarship was rediscovered in a great renaissance of learning. In the pioneer days of North America, colleges and universities appeared spontaneously here and there. They taught the learning of the past, but they did not reach a position of leadership.

Then about a hundred years ago a merchant in Baltimore created a Board of Trustees for a hospital and a university. He did so without supplying any adjectives to describe how these boards should use the prospective endowment. When he died, the largest educational bequest in history, up to that time, came to the Johns Hopkins University.

Mr. Hopkins was a Quaker, an unassuming bachelor of simple tastes. He is reported to have talked one day with Fowler, his English gardener, as follows:

"This estate, Fowler, is to be the site of a great university, a place where the young men of coming generations will have the opportunity which I have always longed for. Young men will study great things here under these trees that thee and I have planted, and yonder, over nearer to the Patapsco, will be a great hospital. I have thought it all out, Fowler. All my family shall be taken care of according to their needs, but after that is done, all I own shall go to these two children of mine, a university and a hospital.

"Like the man in the parable, I have had many talents given to me and I feel they are in trust; I shall not bury them but give them to the lads who long for a wide education and who will do great things someday with the knowledge they receive here in this university. They shall have a chance right here under the shadow of these old trees."*

So, Mr. Johns Hopkins gave funds and freedom to a well-selected board. The members of the board in turn called for advice from Eliot of Harvard University, Angell of Yale and White of Michigan. They suggested nothing new. Daniel Coit Gilman was called to be the president of the new university. Funds and complete freedom were given to that young man. And something akin to inspiration that Eliot and Angell and White had failed to propose, came to him:

He built a university geared to graduate teaching. And, to this end, he seemed to have the gift of "second sight" in the selection of men both young and old. His university contained creators, new professors who were previously unrecognized as leaders, men like William Osler and his colleagues in the medical school, Gildersleeve in classics, and many others. The Johns Hopkins became the first university in the western world capable of competing in creative scholarship with the universities of Europe.

Following the Hopkins example, graduate teaching and research improved, and American and Canadian universities came of age in the eyes of the world. Some degree of genuine leadership came to us then. The initiating impetus for this advance in university work at the graduate level, however, was

---

* A. Flexner, *Daniel Coit Gilman, Creator of the American Type of University*. New York: Harcourt, Brace & Co., 1946.

derived from an endowment gift by a Quaker merchant who also granted freedom in the Grove on the Patapsco.

During the first and second decades of the twentieth century a new phenomenon appeared in the United States. John D. Rockefeller, like Johns Hopkins, decided not to bury the golden talents that had come to him. He created, instead, a remarkable group of Foundations. His declared purpose was "to promote the well-being of mankind throughout the world." Vast sums of money were directed by the trustees to education and to hospitals. The largest single project was the building and development of the first good medical school in China, a project on which the colossal sum of forty-two million was eventually expended. It is a project not forgotten even now in China, for the influence of the Peking Union Medical School is still strong in that country.

The spending by the Rockefeller Foundation all around the world was prompted by altruism and informed realism. No finer thing has emerged in our modern capitalist society. The Montreal Neurological Institute came into existence in 1934 with Rockefeller assistance. But the pattern followed was more important than the money given. The Foundation helped to create it, and left a nucleus of scientific endowment; then it withdrew from the field, leaving the Institute to grow and to live on with local support. It has grown, and will make its independent contribution in a future that has no foreseeable end.

Many other foundations have been created since then. There are, at present, more than eleven thousand such goodly organizations in the United States alone. Most of them are established to make selected gifts and short-term grants. This has provided a beneficial stimulus, of course. But the secret of success in academic work is not to be found in this sort of giving – far from it! Furthermore, objectionable features have developed with the vast increase in short-term grants for research. Heads of departments and even heads of universities are sometimes led into a scramble for these short-term grants. Professors have been known to cut their research projects to fit the whims of those who hand out charity for academic work. The "handouts" are like bribes to induce scholars to work on "this instead of that." Sometimes men even try to run a teaching department on the crumbs that fall from a research grant!

Governments have followed the lead of these foundations on a larger scale. But they have not copied the original Rockefeller Foundation scheme of starting some special work, setting a school or department or an institute on its feet, endowing it and then leaving it to fare as it can with continuing local support – no, not that. They have taken up the giving of short-term grants. That brings annual gratitude which has political advantages. So the Medical Research Council of Britain, the National Research Council in Ottawa, the National Science Foundation in Washington, and more recently the Canada Council have given remarkable temporary emergency assistance to science and a little to original work in the arts.

But direct federal support to universities has also appeared during this era of short-term grants. It has taken different forms in different countries.

Look at the Soviet Socialist Republic first. Support of academies, universities and research institutes is centralized and administered from a federal focus through a system of national academies. The money provided to the professor and to the institutions is often adequate. That is good. The support of student fellowships for the most talented is adequate. That is excellent. But, nevertheless, this is the extreme example of support for ulterior purpose with little freedom. In so far as freedom is limited, the return will be disappointing. There is in Russia little or no independence at the periphery. Research in fields that are not considered important by Moscow would not be supported. Political and philosophical and religious reasoning and writing, if truly independent and frank, would not be encouraged, to say the least.

What is independence without the right to follow lines of thought which those in authority may consider to be a waste of time? What is freedom if one cannot voice opinions contrary to popular dogma? How can universities evolve better things for this world without both freedom and local independence?

In Britain now, with her strong trend to socialism, they stand somewhere between the Russian and the Canadian systems of support. Many millions must be contributed annually from the central government to each university through the University Grants Committee. It must be said at once that the University Grants Committee has always been composed of public-spirited, intelligent citizens. But, nevertheless, grants are made or refused according to the opinions and prejudices of that Committee.

First and last: the most certain guarantee of freedom and independence to any university is endowment. At least half of the financial support of any such institution should come from permanent income arising in invested funds. The investments should be planned for growth so that income will keep pace with rising costs. Grants from governments to universities and institutes should be accompanied by a simultaneous proportional endowment. For every hundred dollars that such an institution receives from government for annual expense and building there should be one hundred dollars of endowment.

At the end of twenty to twenty-five years, with bold investment, would not a university be independent, like the private institutions of the past? The answer to that must be "no." Expansion, growth and rising costs will prevent the government from being discharged so easily of its responsibility.

But that would mean doubling the immediate burden of the financing of higher education! Exactly. The intellectual excellence of the Greeks *can* be bought. But the price is high and the conditions are exacting.

My proposal, I know, would not be accepted by a totalitarian government, and for obvious reasons. It would not be accepted by any government that feared intellectual freedom and independence. In Canada (or in the United States) if even the federal government, in its restricted field of support, were to accept this basis of university assistance it would contribute enormously to the freedom and the independence of higher education. It would do this, moreover, without interfering in the conduct of universities or with the responsibilities of states and provinces.

The price of support – doubling the present costs – would be small indeed when seen in true perspective: money for simultaneous support and endowment, conditions which provide freedom and independence for academic institutions, athletics for all in the growing years, competition for those who are competitive, rewards and applause for excellence in every field of human endeavour, and, with it all, freedom of expression.

Solon, the lawgiver of Athens, counselled the Greeks to lead temperate lives. "Nothing in excess," he said; "all things in due proportion." Let us train the body and use it, train the brain, and turn the mind to the achievement of excellence. If our students and teachers had support, and similar independence with similar rewards, they would do what the classical Greeks did.

But before these things can come about, we must develop a national admiration for that peculiar quality the Greeks called *areté*, admiration for outstanding excellence in any field of human endeavour.

The Approach to Authorship

Creative authorship is an art quite foreign to science-writing and reporting. The scientist or historian who would master it must be prepared, however great his experience, to stumble for a time along a path beset by many a thorny bush and dead-end turn. The objectives of writing in science or history are clear enough. Not so the goal of the fiction-writer.

For historical fiction, the prospective author must do his initial research as in any other field. He must acquire, too, a balanced understanding of men and events. After that, if he is master of the art of authorship, he may create beauty in literary form. He may use devices to captivate the mind of the most careless reader. But he should strive still, as loyally as the writers in the other fields, to represent the truth though he does this by indirection.

Indeed, fiction may make itself more historical than history, when the evidence of what did happen is not complete, as it rarely is. And the novelist who makes himself a scholar in the chosen area may, by bridging gaps in current knowledge, present historical truth as no professional scientist or historian should.

In 1954 a patient who was lying on the examining table in my consulting room looked up at me and asked, "Is there another man of your name in Canada?"

"No, I don't think so." I continued the examination. When I had finished and was turning away she continued her questioning:

"You're not an author, are you?"

FIRST PUBLISHED IN 1961.

I faced her then and confessed that I had written the novel she had seen. She looked at me with an expression I had come to recognize in the faces of other patients, and of friends, when they discovered this professional deviation: surprise, amusement, suspicion, questioning. Could a man serve two masters honourably and well?

In previous years, I had written a number of books on medical and scientific subjects, and many papers. But to the woman on my examining table and to "the man in the street" these would not make me an author. The popular definition, and therefore I suppose the true one, is this: An author is a man who has written a book that people will buy, a book that has meaning for the general reading public.

The distinction is a valid one on other grounds as well. Authorship is a creative art and no man, however experienced in other forms of composition, can hope to deserve the title of author until he has offered the muse his tribute of honest toil. In good time she may grant him the "know-how" and the new insights he needs. And if she takes a fancy to him he may win her smile which means success.

Once, before undertaking that novel, I had tried my hand at what might have been called authorship, not long after my return from study abroad. I dramatized a war experience in the English Channel and sent this literary conception to the *Atlantic Monthly*. It was refused. The editor did not call it a miscarriage. He was more polite than that, but he was firm. This might have been the end as well as the beginning of my approach to authorship – if it had not been for the sadness I saw in a woman's eyes, and a morning in Teheran.

It all came about like this: In 1935 my mother was living in California and I visited her there. For fifteen years or more before that, she had been engaged in writing a novel, her first attempt at authorship. The book was intended to popularize the biblical story of Abraham and Sarah.

On this visit, I found her very frail. She had taken to her bed. The typewriter was ready for use on the over-bed table and the manuscript lay close at hand. But she seemed to have lost her former zest and pleasure in the task. It was clear that illness and age had begun to dull her mind, but not her will.

As she spoke of the unfinished manuscript, there was sadness in her eyes and she passed a trembling hand over her white hair. On the impulse of the moment I took up the manuscript.

"Let me work on it a little. Perhaps we could publish it together."

"Oh," she said, and lay back on the pillow. Her delicate face had lost the anxious look and she smiled. That was all. I brought the manuscript and her source-books back to Montreal with me. But before I found time to examine them, word came that she had passed on – a strong, remarkable woman, who expected much from her younger son; too much, it seemed.

I read the manuscript, found it confused, tried to re-do it. But that proved to be impossible. My additions were like burlap patches on a fragile silk garment. They seemed to tear the material. Her text had been planned for young teen-agers and for that large body of adults whose intellectual evolution lapses in early youth. She understood them and could write for them. But I was too intolerant. So, I put the manuscript away, never to touch it again.

There is a small boy somewhere inside me. I think most men are hiding such a boy away, somewhere. I'm not quite sure where. It may be in the brain, or in the heart, or in the glands for all I know. In any case the small boy did not like it at all when I put that manuscript away. He made me rather unhappy about it. He even argued that I should write a whole new book myself to fulfil her purpose and discharge my promise. I told him I did not know how and did not have time. This was the last subject I would have chosen for a book. Then I forgot it.

Eight years passed and I had done nothing about it, until the twenty-fourth of July, 1943. Curiously enough, I remember that date clearly. It was not because it marked a critical moment in the world war, the pause between the flood tide of the German attack and the ebb that was to lead back to defeat. It was not because I had just left Russia and was forced to wait for air passage to free China on a mission for the Canadian National Research Council. It was not because I had spent the night as the guest of the British Minister in Teheran, Persia.

No, I remember the day for another reason. The morning was very hot and I was walking alone about the Legation garden. That small boy walked back and forth with me, and my mind turned back to the story of Abram and Sarai. After leaving Teheran tomorrow, I reflected, I would be flying over the excavations of Abraham's birth-place. What a chance!

The air was humid. The heat was stifling even in the shade of the sycamore trees. I stared down into a fishpond. Certainly this brief interlude in what I liked to consider my important surgical mission to Moscow and Chungking was not the time to think about Ur of the Chaldees where Abraham was born! And yet – I could think of nothing else.

Fish had come to the surface of the pool and were gasping round and round, as though they too could get no breath. The heat was intolerable. The silence oppressed me. I returned indoors. The Minister, Sir Reader Bullard, had gone out after breakfast on business of the Crown. In the twilight of his library I picked up a paper-covered volume. It was *Ur of the Chaldees*, by Leonard Woolley, the great excavator of that city. I had read the book before, but now, all of a sudden, I saw the people of Sumer as though they were alive. I thought of the thousands of years of rising civilization behind them, these people who gave the world the art of writing and rules of justice. They were about to be destroyed and forgotten at the very time when young Abram and his father, Terah, were planning to leave Ur. Through them, and their Hebrew descendants, this culture was to reach the nations of the west along the slender bridge of the Bible, thus bypassing the civilizations of Athens and Rome.

But, even more exciting than that, there was a secret here, a mystery. What happened to Abram, reared in a land of idol-worship? What caused him to emerge as the founder of monotheism? I would write, I thought, a story of his youth, before his appearance in the Bible, and describe it as it must have been, a romance with all the elements of Sumerian life in it. And in the writing, I would carry out the purposes of a scientific analysis, a historical study. What a challenge! Excitement seized me such as I have rarely known, even in a lifetime of exciting scientific research. I forgot that I did not know how to write fiction. I only knew that I could not wait to start. By the time lunch was called that day I had formulated a plan of action.

Next morning I climbed out of a little Blenheim bomber

aircraft in Habbaniya, Iraq. A transportation officer met me there and gave me orders. I was to proceed to Cairo and wait there eleven days for a plane that would take me on my way back to Basra and across India toward China. I refused. I told him I would make my own way to Basra and catch the Cairo plane there.

The officer argued, but finally he shrugged his shoulders. I was not in uniform, and civilians are always difficult for the military to manage. He would have been certain that the heat had gone to my head if I had pointed out to him my reasons, and the fact that ancient Ur lay between us and Basra. I might have pointed out further, that Basra, at the head of the Persian Gulf, was a seaport with the great marsh behind it and that its setting was much like that of Ur before that city was destroyed by Babylon.

Fortunately I was carrying a letter of introduction to the Principal Medical Officer for Iraq and Iran, Group Captain C. T. O'Neil. I presented it and was ushered into his presence.

"I want to go to the Museum of Archaeology in Baghdad," I told him, "and I simply must visit Ur. I have only eleven days to spend in Mesopotamia."

"Why should anyone want to go to Ur," he asked, "and now of all times? In the spring, it is a very good place to shoot grey rock-pigeons. The desert is covered with flowers then. Now, it is impossible. The diggings have been completely deserted since the war began, and all of Woolley's men have left.

"In any case," he continued abruptly, "there is no way of getting to Ur, and this country is dangerous in the summer heat. There is a war on, you know, and yesterday was the hottest day of the year so far – 121.4 degrees in the shade."

I shook my head. O'Neil looked at me and chuckled. I was wearing a wool suit which had been quite comfortable in Moscow two days before.

"Come along with me," he said. "We will 'make rounds' in the encampment hospital. I have a most interesting ward to show you. It is filled just now with soldiers suffering from heat-stroke."

Group Captain O'Neil proved to be a wise, kindly physician, an Irishman who said my scheme was mad. But he outlined a plan, and set it in motion as only he could do. Next day I flew to Baghdad which was only sixty miles away across the desert.

The Iraq Museum, there, had all the things I wanted to see just then. Its relics told the story of daily life in Sumer four thousand years ago. The curator was a quiet knowledgeable Englishman, Seton Lloyd. He showed me a large block of earth that had been transported, intact, from Ur to the museum. In it was the skeleton of a woman who had been resting there more than four thousand years. At his request, I studied the skull which had been cleared of dust. The sutures where the skull bones come together were easily visible; the brain-case was large; her teeth were beautiful, the bite good. I judged her to be about twenty years of age. There was a handsome necklace of gold and lapis lazuli where once a breast had heaved and a heart throbbed.

Everywhere I turned, facts that had to do with life in the time of Abraham came flooding in on me, facts from which to form the hypotheses of history. Here were the materials for historical fiction. Each day, as I walked back to my hotel along Baghdad's principal street, I was oblivious of the foreign din of honking motor-cars. Instead, I heard the chorus of ancient sounds that echoed, still, from shop and house – the cries of vendors, the *clock, click-clock* of trotting horses, the braying of donkeys, the talk of the men and women who moved with eastern slowness along the narrow ways.

In small cafés the changeless Arab dozed, unmoved by the rising tide of western life about him. And other types of Arabs were there to be seen, men dressed in complete Sheik costume like actors in a western play, handsome, erect, with pointed black beard and hard piercing eyes. These men were watching it all, unconvinced and with ill-concealed contempt.

One day, I stepped out of the midday sun and entered the sudden gloom of MacKenzie's Book Store. It is a western oasis, with its books from ceiling to floor. Here I telephoned back to Habbaniya. O'Neil came on the line.

Yes, he had organized an expedition to Ur and he himself was coming with me. "No trouble at all, I've planned some official business in Basra and this will be on the way. I'll get you to Ur, and then on to Basra in time for the China aircraft!"

Group Captain O'Neil, o.b.e., arrived next day at the Zia Hotel with army cots, mosquito bar, salt, medicine, a huge thermos of water and an expectant smile.

"It's mad," he said, "this trip! But it's all laid on."

Ur Junction is two hundred miles south of Baghdad. It was 4.20 in the morning when our train arrived there. The very phrase, Ur Junction, seemed an anachronism. We were driven to a tented "staging" camp to leave our belongings. Then we climbed back into the army lorry and started off for Ur, only a few miles away. Soon we saw a red hill rising before us. It was set upon a table-land, a mile or more in width. Within that table-land, buried in shifting dust, was Ur, once the greatest centre of culture in all the world, the origin of civilization where brilliant minds devised the art of writing. Once it had been an island washed by the mighty Euphrates. Now it was deserted by man and by the Great River itself – almost forgotten. The symmetrical hill, which proved to be built of red brick, was the Ziggurat of Ur. It had borne on its summit the lovely shrine of the moon god, Nannar.

A flight of stairs has been cut straight up the face of the Ziggurat where the old stairs used to be. We climbed to the top, a height of about twenty metres above the table-land of the city. From here we could look down into the excavations, but the pits were deserted now and dust had long been filling them in.

Far away on the other side of the city one could make out the diggings in the residential area. They looked like little boxes there, arranged in rows, open to the sky. Those were the homes of the well-to-do Sumerians, and in one of them, no doubt, Abram the son of Terah was born.

A hyena emerged from the temple of Nannar below us. He galloped off, stopping from time to time to look back as though wondering who had broken the silence about the altars of the moon god. Sand grouse passed overhead, their brown breasts gleaming in the sun. And in each flock a bird or two kept calling in an ancient tongue: *pitchou, pitcher, pitchou, pitcher* – like the cox of a college boat.

At a little distance, coming from the north, a herd of camels passed, drifting by in stately movement, stopping to graze where the desert showed the yellow of the camel-thorn. An Arab herdsman followed, his cloak flapping in the wind. Blue rock-pigeons rose in whirring flights from subterranean passages. Their nests were there in the royal tombs. They landed on the Ziggurat as they had always done. Nature remained the same. Only man and his works and his civilization had passed away. It was something that could happen to us today. As I stood there on the Ziggurat the men and women I hoped to recall seemed very near.

When I returned to Montreal there was no escape. In my brief-case I had hidden the plot of a novel drawn up in the burning heat of Baghdad. There were only two obstacles in the way now. First, I did not know how to write a novel. Second, there was no time in the life of a busy surgeon who also had a role to play in a busy home and an institute.

I decided to limit this literary project to vacation time, and never to touch it in Montreal. So the manuscript went with me on week-ends in the country and during the usual month of summer holiday. Whenever we travelled about the world, as we did from time to time, I collected more material from museums and libraries. At the end of six years the manuscript of a book, called *No Other Gods*, was finished. As soon as a final copy had been made, I read it. A few friends read it, but they did not need to tell me; I knew. It was a failure, and I had come to a blind-end.

The research had been sufficient. The material was there. But the style! It was stilted. And the book was neither a history nor a novel, but something in between. The actors were wooden, lifeless. What the work lacked was something hidden from me in the art of authorship. But there were good passages in it. I abandoned the writing for a year, but that summer – it was 1949 – my wife and I took a wonderful two-month holiday, returning to Mesopotamia. We rode on camels, and crossed the desert from Damascus to Baghdad (in a bus!). We haunted the Iraq Museum in Baghdad and the waterfront of Basra. We paddled through the reedy channels of the Great Marsh at the head of the Persian Gulf. I visited Ur and climbed the Ziggurat again.

The following year I began to write once more, using the same plot and most of the same characters. But I knew these characters better now. They had gone with us on the journey. I listened to them, letting them talk, and I watched them act and wrote it down, striving for simplicity in diction, reading Shakespeare and hoping to learn how he gained his insights into the minds and hearts of men and women.

We had a little milk-house in the country which was no longer needed to house the cream separator. So we dragged it to a knoll high above the meadows and the lake. There was just room in it for a desk and a chair and a place for a couch and books. I used that for a hide-out. But there was time for the noonday swim and tennis, perhaps, or sailing.

At the end of three years of intermittent work, the manuscript was finished again and I took the precious bundle to the Post Office myself, unwilling to trust it to anyone else.

"It's a manuscript," I said to the postal clerk.

He seemed to understand. "Is this 'Little, Brown' you've written here a publisher?"

"Yes, but they are sure to send it back to me. Then, I suppose, I'll start all over again." He smiled sympathetically.

But they did not send it back. They actually accepted it for publication. And then I discovered that I had lost something. The actors in the book had been going about with me while they matured. They had come to my mind so often in quiet moments, even in Montreal – driving home at night, or in the hush of the operating room when the strain and the risk of losing a life were past. Now they had been taken from me. They would live lives of their own in the minds of other men as long as the book should be read.

The muse had smiled, even though it was from a distance. I knew I was on the path. I could do a better job if I tried again, and perhaps again and again, as long as the years would wait for me. The path my feet had found would lead some day to a second career instead of retirement. So I started another novel. Its goal was to give new life to Hippocrates, the Father of Medicine. Here was a proper task for a physician. Hippocrates had been nearly lost from view in the mists of time. It took five years to write the second novel, while vacations for research and writing became longer and more exciting.

Since that day in Teheran when I accepted my mother's challenge at last, I have come along the writer's path, learning to avoid the thorns and the dead-end turns. All experience can be of use to those who follow that path, and effort brings them skill in the end. But I know now that mastery of the creative art of writing is like infinity, a thing to be forever approached. I am content to be making that approach and to call it a second career.

When spring comes to us here in Quebec, I return to the little milk-house high above Lake Memphremagog. There is no sound but the drone of a passing bee or the distant bell of a cow on the slopes below. When you drop your pen on the page and raise your head for a moment's rest, you smell the earth and growing things. You discover the bobolink's breathless song as he flutters up from the meadow, and the cool deep tones of the thrush from the wood, and the eagle that soars on motionless wing above the lake – and fancy can soar there, too, and back to the page.

The Epic of Alan Gregg

[FIVE]

Seen in long perspective, Alan Gregg's life is an epic of modern times, a splendid adventure in the long, long history of medicine. He was an educator, physician and professional philanthropist, moving freely through the medical centres of the world in a period of momentous change, the like of which will not be known again. During this time, vast private foundations turned the wealth of capitalism to the service of mankind through medical channels; and governments began to follow their lead on a larger scale, imitating and, in the end, beginning to displace private philanthropies.

Throughout this period Gregg, drawing on his exhaustive first-hand knowledge, counselled giver and receiver alike, activated always by the high purposes of science and compassion. Thirty years ago, his arrival in any medical school sent a ripple of excitement through it, from Dean down to lowly but hopeful experimenter and teacher. Gregg brought with him the possibility of a Rockefeller grant or endowment for original work. His very name had the warm overtones of hoped-for favours to come. But even when no money was involved, his favourable comment carried with it the stamp of approval by a high and independent authority.

In general I knew him as the other men in university medicine knew him. We admired him, a somewhat lonely figure, a whimsical man who told amusing stories, as Abraham Lincoln did, to punctuate his purposes. But the idea of writing his

THE FOURTH ALAN GREGG MEMORIAL LECTURE, ASSOCIATION OF AMERICAN MEDICAL COLLEGES; MONTREAL, NOVEMBER 1961.

biography had never occurred to me until his wife proposed it in May 1959, almost two years after his death. "Alan's biography," she wrote, "could be a delightful, worthwhile undertaking for someone who knew, and admired and loved him." The letter closed with these words: "As Alan would say – Don't answer until you've passed through the negative stage!"

My initial reaction was to refuse. Almost a year later, in March 1960, I was still in the "negative stage," but I decided to reconnoitre. So my wife and I visited Big Sur, California. The Greggs had retired there, to what they thought the loveliest place of all. There, death had come to Alan Gregg all too soon. I could, I thought, at least talk to Mrs. Gregg. She had remained in their new home and I could open his file and read his thoughts and see in retrospect, as though from within, the life that I had glimpsed from without.

The Gregg house is a thousand feet above the sea, perched half way up the slope of the coast range. Turning from the scenic highway that runs between San Francisco and Los Angeles, you drive through a gate into the Gregg road. It passes under tall pines and eucalyptus trees to a small ranch-house built of redwood, with pleasant roofs and a welcoming patio. The whole house was built of one mighty redwood tree, cut into appropriate sizes of lumber. Along the road, blue ceanothus was in bloom and in the patio there were climbing roses. A California jay announced our arrival in raucous tones of derision. But Eleanor Gregg, tanned and smiling, came to meet us.

We followed her through the house and left it by another door to find ourselves on a terrace floored with circular redwood blocks. The panorama, when we raised our eyes, made us exclaim and stand speechless. A thousand feet below and to the right, the Pacific Ocean glittered in the sun and a white line of surf, edging the shore, ran away to the south until it faded into the mist. Directly above us towered a mountain wall capped with rounded peaks against the blue sky. Smooth green slopes broken by deep parallel ravines ran steeply down to the ocean shore.

When they bought this house, the Greggs had added a study to it. It opened on this terrace. Here were Alan Gregg's files and here he had planned to write and reflect through years of formal retirement. Here, he would write his books, serious, philosophical, amusing – the books he had always dreamed of writing and had outlined in those rare idle moments that came to him in his crowded life.

He had plans and outlines for four books – Notes on Giving, a comprehensive book on medical education, an autobiography, a children's story that would enlarge a remarkable childhood fantasy about three strange races of people called the Trobans, the Bibbits and the Brogans.

Each night he and his wife slept on that terrace under the stars. At dawn, he rose to busy himself with his many projects. One of them was to record just where the sun appeared on the skyline. His chart shows the progress of the sun's appearance along that lofty rim of the world which seems so close and intimate there. He noted the dates and names of the peaks – one of them reminded him of Pike's Peak which he had known so well in his boyhood in Colorado Springs, and he named it that. It was natural enough for them to have returned to this, after many travels through the world. Not very far away, in Carmel, they had been married. Their honeymoon had been spent wandering through the redwood forests of the coast.

One day as I sat on the terrace deck with Eleanor Gregg, I asked her to draw a profile of him in her own words to help me with the task that I was considering. She sat for a little time in thought.

"When I first knew him at sixteen his features were unformed. But Alan changed with the years. In time his wonderful character set its own imprint on his face."

She paused, and I watched a lizard darting across the redwood stumps on the terrace deck. She looked away into the distance. The wind was sending waves of silver light over the green shoulder of the nearest ridge, waves that billowed through the wild oats planted, it is said, by the Spanish explorers who came to this coast four centuries ago. Gust after gust moved across it and upward toward the top. A lonely buzzard soared down on motionless wings out of the distant blue.

"He was always a picture of health," she continued, "ruddy complexion, red hair, very white teeth. He freckled and burned

so easily in the sun. He had a fine speaking voice, broad
shoulders, very deep chest. He was intelligent and so unexpected but always kind in what he said – and humour! His
humour was always bubbling up."

She laughed. "I don't believe any woman ever laughed so
much. We laughed all the way through the thirty-three years
that we were married. We had such fun.

"People noticed his eyebrows. Of course they became more
bushy as time passed. He seemed to look through you. Often
I noticed he looked past people he was talking to but he could
describe every detail of face and feature. I learned to be
observant – from him.

"It isn't lonely here. I have so much to occupy my mind, so
many books to read, his papers to put in order. And it's always
so beautiful. I still sleep out here on the deck under the stars.
There is plenty to keep me busy with garden and house. That
reminds me – it is nearly time for lunch."

She disappeared into the house. The buzzard was soaring
swiftly down the slope and passed from sight among the red-
woods in the ravine, answering some mysterious summons in
the shadows below.

Surely no one can know a man as his wife does. Should not
the wife be the best person to write a man's biography? Or does
emotion make it difficult to tell his story in true perspective?
Perhaps there are sides of a man that no wife could describe
dispassionately, sides perhaps that she cannot even see. Alan
Gregg had thought of writing his own biography – many men
think of such a thing and never get to it. Some things a man
knows best about himself. But after all, which is the real man –
the man of thoughts and hopes and dreams; or the man of
performance and achievement?

A life, like any other project in literature or science, requires
first exhaustive research and later the hoped-for understanding.
Well, here are the data, the when and the where of his life in
briefest outline. Alan Gregg, American physician, educator and
medical philanthropist, was born in Colorado Springs July 11,
1890, son of James Gregg, a Congregational minister in that
city; educated at Cutler Academy, Colorado Springs, Harvard
College, Harvard Medical School. Internship at Massachusetts

General Hospital. In 1917, enlisted as Medical Officer with a Harvard medical unit in Britain's Royal Army Medical Corps. In 1919, he joined the International Health Board of the Rockefeller Foundation under Dr. Wickliffe Rose and was sent to Brazil for three years' work in public health. In 1922, returning from New York, became Associate Director of Medical Education. July 1923, married Eleanor Barrows, daughter of a clergyman who was subsequently President of Oberlin College. During 1924 to 1930, the Greggs lived in Europe and he was attached to the Paris office of the Rockefeller Foundation making a unique study of medical education throughout Europe. From 1931 to 1951, Director of the Division of Medical Sciences, Rockefeller Foundation. From 1952 to 1956, Vice-President, Rockefeller Foundation; after which he retired. At last on June 19th, 1957, death at his home in Big Sur, California.

In the thirty-seven years of his association with the Rockefeller Foundation, it is fair to say that he became the leading philanthropist in the field of medical education and research. But in his own right, as the result of his vast experience, he was for a considerable period the world's foremost consultant to those who were concerned with the future of medicine and education.

There you have the skeleton. Who can give it muscle, sinews, brain, and add to that a man's mind and will, his happiness and sorrow? Who is it sees a man most clearly, and who should tell his story? The man himself? His wife? His child? His friend? A colleague? A disciple? Or a stranger? Each has an image all his own – none is quite like any other. What I may write after long inquiry could never read like the autobiography he might have written, nor contain quite the same substance. What Alan Gregg would want, I feel sure, is that someone should spell out his purposes, in his chosen field, and his conclusions.

Let me turn to his antecedents for a moment, and particularly the women of his family. The Greggs seem to have wived very well. As far back as I can trace Alan's ancestors, they selected and married strong, able women. It seems to have been the influence of a strong woman that brought the Greggs from Scotland to New England in the first place. There was a James

Gregg who lived in Scotland seven generations before Alan. He was a young man when this story begins and had learned the tailoring trade, setting up a shop in Ayrshire. Now, that was half a century before the poet Robert Burns was born there. But the charms that Burns described so well were certainly known to men before his time.

Fortunately for the tailors of that day, it was the custom that they should make garments for women as well as for men. One day an elderly gentleman came to the shop of James Gregg with his daughter who was, it is written, "a comely maiden." Would the young man show her all his best materials and make up everything that she might need for a trousseau in preparation for her approaching marriage? Then the gentleman, being a man of some substance, hurried off about his business. When he had gone, the tailor discovered, to his surprise, that his client was not at all enthusiastic about the matter. It seemed that her father had not done well when he selected the bridegroom. The man was far too old, too unattractive, to make the event very exciting.

But, after a little talk, the prospective bride decided to carry out her father's plan in regard to the trousseau. The choice of materials made frequent visits necessary, and the fittings that followed were numerous and altogether delightful. Her apathy vanished. Her glances and smiles must have wakened, in James Gregg, strange untailor-like thoughts, feelings like those that came to Rabbie Burns on the banks of Bonnie Doon.

However, he worked hard and made many suggestions while the trousseau grew to a great pile. The young lady made other suggestions. It is quite likely that she suggested to her father that he should pay the bill for the trousseau before the wedding. On the last day before the wedding, she showed the complete trousseau to her family and friends with great excitement. It was much admired.

But on the following day the trousseau had vanished, the bride had vanished, and the tailor had closed his shop forever. James Gregg was on his way to northern Ireland, and Janet Cargill went with him from Illa in Ayrshire to Londonderry and there they were married. But that was evidently not the end of Janet's suggestions to the young man. They had children, and he became a "bleacher of linen, and in due time, amassed a tidy little fortune." Now, all that occurred just before 1700. In 1718, they sailed from Belfast to Boston to settle, with other families of Scotch-Irish stock, on either side of the West-running Brook in New Hampshire. Captain James Gregg, as he was called after fighting against the Indians, was buried in 1758 in his eighty-fifth year in the cemetery of Londonderry, New Hampshire.

The grandfather of Alan was also named James. He married a remarkable woman late in life. She was his first cousin on his mother's side, and so a double dose of English Bartlett entered the inheritance. But at the end of three years, when his son James, who was to be Alan's father, was only two years of age, he was killed in a railroad accident. Not long after that, all of his buildings were burned in a dreadful fire on the Mystic River in the town of Medford. It is now included in Greater Boston and the great throughway passes over the Mystic River at the spot.

Mary Bartlett Gregg, left penniless at the age of forty-eight with a two-year-old son, was not to be daunted. She would see to it that he had the best education obtainable, and she did. The boy graduated from Andover Academy and Harvard University while she kept a boarding-house in Medford, Andover and Cambridge in patient succession. The career of Alan Gregg began in the quiet courage of this admirable woman and in the scholarship and sterling character of her son, his father.

In 1950, Alan Gregg at the age of sixty looked backward and forward while returning to the United States on board ship. He made some notes in the quiet of his cabin, taking stock of life. "I have five more years to work in the Rockefeller Foundation," he wrote. "I know myself well enough to suspect that unless I make an extra effort they will be years of diminuendo, not crescendo. . . . So, for clarity and alacrity's sake, it might be worthwhile to outline a program for the home stretch."

First, if he could make others see, he wrote, "the importance of endowing a few big things instead of frittering the money away in many small projects, I could finish a few of the really significant undertakings with endowments, instead af grants."

After some further observations, he added: "but a much more important consideration dominates my view of the next five years' work. I can be more useful to medicine the world over in the capacity of consultant and adviser on the objectives and organization of medical education and medical research . . ."

Finally he wrote: "There still remains a quite different kind of work I could do, and do from a range of experience that no one else has been fortunate enough to have. I have been in steady and often intimate contact with medical schools over 27 years in many countries . . . In most of these countries medical education is changing if it is not growing. There is an excellent opportunity for a book on medical education written from such an experience but pointed to the future. I can write fairly well if I work at it hard. That would seem to me the best use of my time."

Six years of life did, in fact, remain to him. But the "diminuendo" that he had feared came, based on failing capacity. The book to present his experience and his advice for others, the book pointed toward the future, was never written.

I was a beggar when I first came to know Alan Gregg, and he a professional philanthropist. In 1931, while he was still in Paris, Richard Pearce, his beloved chief in the Rockefeller Foundation, died, and Gregg was recalled from Paris to succeed him as Director of the Division of Medical Sciences. He reached New York in September and moved his family to Scarsdale.

In the "unfinished business" on his predecessor's desk, he must have found an application from McGill University for considerably more than a million dollars to help create the Montreal Neurological Institute. On October 13, he came to Montreal. I met him at the train, to take him home to breakfast. The man who came walking down the platform toward me was a Scot if I ever saw one – sandy, freckled, broad-shouldered, with a quick laugh and a level blue-eyed gaze. I have seen just that type among the men in the Isle of Skye in Scotland's Western Islands, men who might pass for his brother;

evidence, no doubt, that Scandinavian Vikings passed that way. Although two of his grandparents had the blood of those English Bartletts, the Scottish Greggs had certainly triumphed in outward form.

After breakfast, he drew the McGill application from his brief-case. "This is exactly what we want to carry out." He said more in the same vein, as though to convince me that we were doing the Rockefeller Foundation a very great favour. He was vigorous, quick, perceptive, friendly. His speech was blunt and full of chuckles. It was clear at once that here was a man who did not want to be thanked except in terms of results.

In the years that followed that first meeting I saw him only at long intervals, but Alan Gregg was a friend you never forgot, a friend who did not change. He was the sort of man you turned to for wise counsel, even in private problems, and I did that more than once. What I saw in him, before considering the possibility of writing his biography, was gay humour, sincerity, simplicity, common sense, wisdom gained from vast experience and unflagging labour – and beneath it all a certain wistful loneliness, or was it a sense of weakness where others saw only strength?

When the Montreal Neurological Institute was opened in 1934, he did not appear, in spite of urgent invitations; and he sent no representative. But in 1953, when the new McConnell wing was opened, doubling the size and capacity of the Institute, he came and spoke. He felt he could come because this expansion was something to which his Foundation had made no contribution. It was the spontaneous growth he had hoped for and gambled on.

He thanked the staff for what they had done, not recognizing the gratitude we felt to him and, through him, to that Foundation in New York which has set before the world such a magnificent example of altruism.

"Goethe," Gregg said with a smile, "held that it is important to know as much as possible about what you want most of all, because sooner or later you are so likely to obtain it."

He turned to the general problem of the support of education and research with these words:

"I believe that endowment, whether from government or private sources, is the soundest way to secure optimum results when it is certain the work to be done is needed. The steady confidence, that is conferred by endowment, calls out from scientists honesty and steadfastness of purpose: the hesitant uncertainty of short-term grants all but insults the intelligence, if not the sincerity, of the recipient and certainly makes a mockery of long-term planning.

"Experience," he continued, "is our teacher in this matter. Indeed it cannot be news to some of you that a reaction has set in against short-term grants. They have favoured hasty work on trivial questions. They dissuade the more honest and circumspect young men from entering investigative careers – that is my considered judgment."

That was his indictment of modern trends in the support of academic and research institutions. It is an indictment that I echo with all my heart and mind. We made our approaches, he and I, from different directions, he a philanthropist and I a beggar. He became an adviser on the directions of research and I an investigator. He was a consultant to educational institutions and hospitals and I a teacher and practitioner. And yet our conclusions were the same. Because of that I shall undertake to tell his story as well as I can, and so present his conclusions, and mine.

Sir William Osler

During his later years Sir William Osler was a hero to the rising generation of medical men, and after his death biographers heaped his shrine high with tributes, higher than the hero himself would have liked, no doubt. And so, for those who did not know him, I fear this fulsome praise may have obscured the simplicity and the charm of the man.

Some of the material to be presented here may seem sophomoric; but it is new, for contemporary descriptions of Osler by his own students are rare. Perhaps this is because greatness close at hand may pass as commonplace; perhaps it is only that the undergraduate perceives the danger of expressing his opinion of his teachers (at least in public). Even the charming letters of J. B. MacCallum, written when he was a student at Johns Hopkins (1896-99), contain only occasional references to the professor of medicine, as in the following example:

> I was called up in Osler's Clinic. . . . They are the nicest things we go to, for Dr. Osler sits on the table and swings his feet, and asks you all sorts of questions you have never heard before. . . . Dr. Osler's clinics are splendid. It is so nice to hear him talk to the patients. He has a joke for everyone.

And again, when young MacCallum himself was Osler's patient, he wrote, "You can't get anything out of him. He is always talking such a lot of nonsense."

AN ADDRESS TO THE OSLER SOCIETY, UNIVERSITY OF WESTERN ONTARIO; JANUARY 1941.

From the unpublished letters of another medical under-graduate, I have culled more extended references to Osler, during his Oxford period. I seem to remember this student well enough, but I hardly realized how naïve he was until I came on these letters, written to his mother. The young American had heard a little of Osler's heroic past; so his first reaction was one of surprise to find him an ordinary man, like other men. One week after beginning his medical studies, he wrote, from his rooms in Merton College, Oxford:

> [January 1915] When I look up at the seven volumes of Osler's Medicine on my shelf, it makes me, mentally, worship him. It does not seem possible that he can be the same middle-aged man I saw last Sunday, who, with a room full of guests, spent most of his time in pretending to bandage up the leg of a young officer, to the glee of two little children.
>
> Sir William said to me: "Don't you go to the Front; you have got to use all your vacations in real work. I'm going to watch you and see that you don't go home any vacations," so I guess I'm committed to vacations in Edinburgh and will see little work in France.

At the end of a year in Oxford, December 1915, the student wrote:

> Sir William had the students of his department out to his home one evening and he talked very interestingly about the origination of Physical Diagnosis and showed us some of his priceless collection of early manuscripts and writings of doctors, old Latin things, for Latin was the only written language of medicine for a long while.
>
> [January 1916] Davison* just came in and said that Osler had 'phoned him and asked if he and I would not like to go down to Cliveden with him tomorrow; it means cutting one lab., but of course I will go. He goes to Cliveden each week to inspect the big Canadian Hospital there.

---

* Wilburt C. Davison, then Oxford undergraduate, later Dean and organizer of the Faculty of Medicine, Duke University.

And, again, in February:

> Sir William told the story of his life last night, at a meeting of the American Club, simply, with no affectation nor false modesty. He said he started with every opportunity, seventh in a missionary's family [the student misquoted; Sir William was the eighth child], with twins ahead. He took time for a "gilt-edged" degree and for working too. When the Hopkins was being built, he was at the University of Pennsylvania Medical School. He said one morning Dr. Billings walked into his room and said: "Osler, we are opening the Johns Hopkins in a month; will you go down and take charge of the School of Medicine with Welch?" Osler said: "Will I? Yes." "All right, someone will write you, good morning."
>
> When he was in England in 1904, and tired almost to death with the work and engagements of Baltimore, they offered him this job here (the Chair of Regius Professor of Medicine). So he cabled his wife. Her answer was characteristic – it was, "Don't procrastinate; accept at once. Better to leave Baltimore in a ship than in a wooden box." So he accepted.
>
> He said, at the end, that *his rule had been to like and sympathize* with everyone. That's his creed, I think. He is the least sentimental and the most helpful man I've ever seen – the most lovable. You may believe that he is stimulating to me, too, and is on something of a pedestal. If I were not so dumb, I should have the nerve to hope and dream I might follow in his footsteps.

On March 24, 1916, while crossing the Channel for a second trip to a Red Cross hospital in France, the student was wounded when his ship was torpedoed. He was returned to a military hospital, in Dover, from which he wrote as follows:

> This is easily the best ward in the hospital. I am learning lots, lots. Bedside manner, I think I've discovered, is nothing but the effect of the doctor's personality. A young, handsome doctor left me hating him after three minutes of hurried examination. It was not that he did not know, but that he did not care about me, or my feelings . . .

My! everyone is nice. Both Sir William and Lady Osler and their cousin have written and Sir William telephoned.

[April] Received my first bunch of flowers. The first ever. They came from Lady Osler. I can hardly understand all their kind attention. A letter came from him yesterday to tell me about the surgeon who is in charge of me, Mr. Linington. He says he seems to be a good man, to judge from his directories, and he remembered an article by Linington in the *Lancet* and told me to ask the latter about it. So I did, and he seemed quite pleased and brought it for me to read. This morning, Mr. Linington said he had heard directly from Sir William.

That was his way of helping, from behind the scenes. A month later, it was the student's unbelievably good fortune to find himself in the Osler home at Norham Gardens, where he wrote on Easter morning:

It is good to be so near Sir William. He does not dislike anyone. He sees good and something to admire in everyone, and I've seen his face cloud up when someone repeated a bit of scandal or criticism. He is full of vigor and energy.

Last night he came into my room about 10 o'clock, as he has each night, in the red smoking jacket. I showed him an X-ray photograph and simple photograph of one of my ten cases at Ris Orangis, which Dr. Blake [Dr. Joseph Blake, then chief surgeon of Hôpital Militaire V.R.76 and formerly a surgeon in New York] had operated on. He said it was unique, and advised me to publish it!

Breakfast comes to me in bed. He forbids my getting up before. The silver and the little portions seem good after Dover. Soon Revere and Sir William both come in to see what they can do. Revere is a captain in the R.A.M.C. but is home on leave waiting his change into the artillery. After I am dressed, Lady Osler comes in to talk a little. Never before have I been waited on like this. If I enter a room, Lady Osler gets me a pillow, and someone else a footstool, etc., until I sit down quickly in a sort of shame.

Much of the nice days I spend on the terrace overlooking the garden and Oxford Parks. I never heard such birds as here in England. It is like a great choir, the quality of whose voices is ever changing. I read Physiology, or, perhaps, one of the books Sir William has brought me, on the endocrine organs. One of them is in Italian, a great tome, but I look at the pictures and puzzle out a few words.

Two little kiddies came in to see "William," as they call Sir William, the other day and, to amuse them, he took them up to a second storey porch which overlooks the garden, and from there he threw water down on Lytle and Davison, who had come to see me. Then, when Lytle put up a lady's umbrella, which lay there, he poured a whole pitcher of water full on him, while the kiddies screamed with delight.

After this two weeks' idyll, the student moved back into his Oxford lodgings, but the kindness that emanated from the Osler household did not cease. Revere Osler once came in after a day's fishing on the Thames and left a trout for him. In a short time he wrote:

Let me tell you what Sir William has done now. He had Davison and me to tea Thursday afternoon, and then we went down to his office in the Museum. Here was a great collection of medical books and of his own reprints. The books were about to be sent to the University of Louvain. "Now," he said, "you boys had better take what books you like, about 20 apiece, and take a set of reprints," and he went off with his springy step, waving his hand as he slammed the door to cut off our attempted thanks. We took off our coats and dove in, carrying off 40 and, later, splitting them in my room. I have a dandy two-volume surgery, etc. etc. . . . But the reprints are the best of all. You've no idea what that man has written on – almost every topic in medicine. And now he tells us to bring the reprints to tea this afternoon, and he will send them away to have each set bound and titled.

I shall never do it, but I'd like to get a first class in the final examinations because of what Sir William will think.

In these youthful letters there is nothing very extraordinary, but they tell one why every medical man and student who knew him loved him and resolved to emulate him. Osler was a simple man, who never made his juniors conscious that they were in the presence of greatness. What is more important, I think that he himself never gave a thought to the length of his own shadow. He had too lively a sense of humour for that, and, besides, he was much too busy following his own rule of life, "to like and sympathize with everyone."

In the summer of 1917 the medical student had found his way to Paris. There he received a letter from Lady Osler:

You will, I know, grieve for us when you hear that Revere died August 30th from wounds. It is too horrible to take in, and yet we expected it. I prayed Sir William might be spared this. We know little yet. The first news came from Major Harvey Cushing, who was with him at the c.c.s., and that comforts us so much. I am bothering you – by asking you to do this for me – but know you will not mind. So many of Sir William's friends are in France, and I know all will have the New York Herald (Paris edition), and so I am asking you to put this among the death notices:

"Died of wounds received in Belgium, Edward Revere Osler, 2nd Lieut., Royal Field Artillery, aged 21. Son of Sir William Osler, Bt., Regius Professor of Medicine at Oxford, and of Lady Osler."

That the death of his only child and dear comrade was the greatest sorrow that life brought to Sir William seems obvious. But, although his nights were passed in agony, that house, which had gained the name of "The Open Arms," an asylum which had continuously shut its guests away from the worries and cares of war-time, did not now become a place of lamentation.

The week-end after the receipt of the news of Revere's death has been described by Dr. Robert Osgood, of Boston. When he

heard the news, he immediately proposed to recall his accept-
ance of an invitation to visit Oxford, but he was informed that
both Sir William and Lady Osler would be "distressed and
almost displeased" if he did not come. Therefore, with mis-
givings, Dr. Osgood carried on with the visit, which he
described* as follows:

> Sir William met me on the Oxford platform, gay,
> debonair, with a flower in his button-hole, and, as we
> drove to Norham Gardens, was as scintillating, humorous
> and charming as he possibly could be, without a sugges-
> tion of any lurking sadness.
>
> Soon we dressed for dinner, at which there were
> perhaps half a dozen guests who were spending the
> week-end, including a scholar, whose name I have for-
> gotten, connected with the British Museum, a Canadian
> lieutenant, who was just having his leave from his regi-
> ment in London, and myself. It was a very merry dinner
> party, and Lady Osler seemed as completely in control of
> herself and her emotions as did Sir William.
>
> After dinner, when the gentlemen had gone upstairs to
> smoke in Sir William's library, he would pull down a
> non-medical book from his shelves and ask the scholar
> from the Museum something about it and his opinion
> concerning it, and it would be quite evident in a few
> minutes that Sir William was very much the more con-
> versant with this non-medical book. He would then touch
> on some medical subject and address me, and I would, of
> course, scuttle as gracefully as I could beneath his feet.
> He would then turn to the Canadian lieutenant and dis-
> cuss with him the size of Gertie Miller's ankles (she was
> then the leading vaudeville star) and he had considerably
> more knowledge of their size and pulchritude than the
> young lieutenant.
>
> So the evening went. With the ladies he was again, of
> course, the brilliant leader of conversation. . . .

* Personal communication from Robert Osgood, distinguished American
orthopaedist.

That night Dr. Osgood slept little; at dawn, before others were stirring, he dressed and left his room to go for a walk in the Parks. As he passed on tiptoe down the hall he was startled to see, through the crack of a slightly opened door, Sir William, kneeling in silence by his bed.

> ... Sunday, Lady Osler went to church. There was another very considerable party at luncheon. In the afternoon twenty-five American aviators were in for tea with gaiety unconfined.
>
> It was almost more than one could bear, this apparent gaiety, this complete obscuration of his real feelings, because it was war-time and the sporting thing to do. Lady Osler entirely caught his spirit and talked and acted in complete harmony with his mood. I fancy efforts like this may have lost him to the world too early.

Aequanimitas! That was the word he had inscribed on his own crest when he was created a baronet. *Aequanimitas* was an essential quality in his character. He did not strain to do more than he could, but took all things in his stride – even the death of Revere.

Sir William Osler devoted his mind to medical education, to the study of clinical problems and to the lore of medical history. In all those fields he was a distinguished leader, and yet it is not altogether because of these qualities of the intellect that Osler Societies have sprung up in so many parts of the English-speaking world, chiefly composed of students or of young physicians. The unique quality of this man had to do with the "heart."

I would have you see him, through the eyes of the previously quoted undergraduate, as "the least sentimental, the most helpful, most lovable," teacher of medicine. He belongs to medical students of all time, as Lincoln belongs to common men everywhere, a man who grew to be what he was by dint of hard work, and in whose footsteps any undergraduate may dare to "hope and dream" that he may follow.

*　　*　　*

In the autumn of 1919, that medical student returned to Oxford. He had become a qualified doctor keen to carry on with graduate study. But Sir William was ill with pneumonia acquired on a difficult journey as a medical consultant, and the student never saw him again. A few weeks later, he watched men bear the body of the Regius Professor of Medicine across the great quadrangle of Christ Church and into the college chapel.

He followed and sat in a dark corner of the chapel. During the service he leaned against the cold stone with a feeling of great loneliness, remembering at how many points his student life had been touched by this man, how often his spirit had been lifted.

As the years pass and I read Osler's addresses that range beyond the field of medicine, a deeper understanding comes and the companionship means more and more to me.

Sir Charles Sherrington

[SEVEN]

Others have memorialized him as a physiologist. I shall describe the man as I knew him and as he is revealed in his more personal writings late in life: the sensitive schoolboy, sturdy athlete, traveller, lover of art, investigator, teacher, scholar, raconteur, many-sided genius – Sir Charles Sherrington, Physiologist, Philosopher, Poet.

Let me begin with Sherrington the poet, for it is through his little book of verse (Sherrington, 1925) that one may see this modest man most clearly. A poet is alive to hidden meanings, to mystery and romance as well as to facts, regardless of how little he may publish. I suppose he is still a poet if he writes nothing for others. It is remarkable that Sherrington's book of poems appeared first when he was sixty-eight. And yet he had always been a poet. "The fairest thoughts," he wrote, "are still the thoughts unspoken."

His gems of thought sparkle with rare beauty, although the poetic chain on which they hang is sometimes made of strange metals. I fancy that when he left his busy laboratory on a sunny spring day and cycled home, or walked of an evening in Oxford, or looked from his window at dawn in London or in Liverpool, his thoughts were often those of a poet rather than of a philosopher or physiologist:

> *Look at the stars, yet look not there too long,*
> *they have in them where the soul can drown.*

AN ADDRESS TO THE CANADIAN NEUROLOGICAL SOCIETY; SASKATOON, JUNE, 1957.

What a horizon he must have seen from his many-windowed mind! He must have mastered the secret of concentration, as well as inhibition, when so many prospects tempted him:

What song was that of old the Sirens sang,
the song the wise Ulysses would not hear,
gripping his helm-oar steady as a spear,
watching his bellied wind-sheet lest it hang!

.   .   .   .   .

Wise then are they who shun the Siren's cry,
– ah, wiser yet who follow it till they die!

At Oxford, Lady Sherrington rented a punt for the season on the near-by river. She and her husband loved the hidden reaches of the Cherwell and the Isis, those streams that wander through the meadows and finally flow together to give birth to the Thames. They often punted there on pleasant summer evenings and "Carr", the son, went with them when he was small. And so, with picnic baskets, they would slip away along the lazy drifting waterways, watching the beauty, breathing the fragrance, listening to the soft swish of the whispering banks and, high in the blue above, the song of the lark. The ancient tower of the Iffley church must have looked down on them, more than once, as they slipped past beneath the willows.

In 1916, Sir Charles wrote:

I passed beside the Norman church,
above me sang the vesper bell,
the grey place smiled as with nun's joys
                    dropped beads o'ertell.
Such old enchantment as a boy's
when life first whispers use of life . . .

Lovely fancies – the sound of vesper bell, nun's joys, a boy's enchantment "when life first whispers use of life." His scientific writing and lecturing was a little like that too, precious thoughts in so close a succession that it was sometimes difficult for the untutored listener to follow.

In the laboratory he did not talk of the thoughts that must have crowded in upon him, pedalling home to Chadlington Road for lunch:

> *What of noon's full, when the crowned summer day*
> *finger on lip, holds silent field and bower ...*

The longest of his poems, called "The Assaying of Brabantius", was written at about the time his son was married and sailed away to America, where he accepted a teaching post at Cornell University. Thoughts that had to do with this sad parting appear on every page.

Sherrington had been married to Ethel Wright of Preston, Suffolk, in 1891, when he was thirty-five years old. She was a high-spirited girl, a great enthusiast for sport, a good companion. Love finds ample reference in his poetic writings:

> *Loving is more than living, more than to be beloved.*

And again he wrote in a poem entitled "If love were all then well it were":

> *For what were love if no toil were,*
> *and what were life without the sea,*
> *a sheet unbent, a tall mast bare,*
> *a spice-freight rotting top the quay?*
> *Then hoist the sail, and sink the shore,*
> *let be for love its meed anon,*
> *but first for us the stormed sea-floor,*
> *salt winds behind, salt waves before,*
> *salt planks to foot upon.*

One may surmise that loneliness, following the death of Ethel, prompted the following verses:

> *Loud thrush, and there was once a day*
> *she heard you o'er the garden sing,*
> *and, looking up from where she lay,*
> *said 'I am glad it is the Spring.'*

And now the spring, and springs to be,
  and all the springs that ever were,
discourse her music uselessly,
  for ever nothing shall she care.

It is not true that his mind had many compartments. Rather one should say that this was a man who could open the windows of his soul one way, or another, and serve the causes of separate masters faithfully.

When he was engaged in research, no scientist was ever less a poet. In the laboratory he observed and pondered the facts before him and tested them, doubting till the answer was clear. He did not leap to unproven conclusions nor give scope to poetic intuition there. When he turned to philosophy, reason was his guide. Facts were facts and rationalizations well considered.

It is fortunate for us that he accepted an invitation to give the Silliman Memorial lectures at Yale in 1904, "an annual course of lectures designed", according to the terms of the bequest, "to illustrate the presence and the providence, the wisdom and goodness of God, as manifested in the natural and moral world"; fortunate for us, particularly, because he accepted the accompanying demand of publication.

Considering the terms of the bequest, he might well have written a philosophical treatise. But, instead, the "Integrative Action of the Nervous System" which resulted was a model of reasoned biological science. When the Physiological Society republished it, forty-one years later, Samson Wright wrote in the editorial note that their purpose was to make it live again so that it might be read "by all students of physiology and be re-read by their teachers and by mature investigators in the field."

In 1937 when he accepted the Gifford Lectureship, he wrote a philosophical treatise, "Man On His Nature", although the terms of that lectureship were not so very dissimilar to those of the Silliman Lecture. A charming little book on Goethe was the result of a request for publication when he lectured at Lady Margaret Hall, Oxford. The biography of Jean Fernel was, I suppose, a by-product of his reading during the preparation of his Gifford Lectures. What a pity no more demands were made on his time, during this fertile octogenarian decade that followed retirement from physiology!

What was it that made Sherrington able to turn from one field to another with such brilliant achievement? Much of the secret, certainly, is to be found in the history of his boyhood and youth; a man may become a good linguist if he has heard and used several languages in the plastic period of childhood. To my way of thinking, Sherrington's career is a strong argument for the belief that a broad schooling in the humanities is the best preliminary training for medical men or for medical scientists.

Charles's father died when he was a youngster. No doubt, the bond between son and mother was made doubly strong by this misfortune. This is borne out by his poem "Mother and Son" written before she died. The family moved to Ipswich, and their home there, Edgehill House, was a rendezvous for those interested in art, archaeology and geology. The house was filled with excellent paintings, some of which hang now in the Gallery at Norwich.

As he grew older, Charles became a strong and expert athlete, playing soccer for the Town of Ipswich and, later, rugger for St. Thomas's Hospital. While at Cambridge, he rowed for his college, Caius. He also found time for sailing. He was a pioneer in winter sports and made occasional trips to Grindelwald for that purpose until nearly forty years of age.

At Cambridge he studied physiology under Michael Foster who, to use the words of Sharpey-Schäfer, "would make the bones of biological science live again." He took the degree of B.A. in 1884 and two years later qualified in medicine (M.B., Cambridge). He began his research while an undergraduate, working with Langley who was then setting out on his own work on the nervous system.

When he qualified in medicine, Sherrington was twenty-eight years of age. He went to Spain and to Italy to investigate outbreaks of cholera and, while there, found time for art as well as pathology. He studied in Germany under Virchow, Koch, Waldeyer, Zuntz. He made several trips later on to study in Strassburg with Golz. At thirty he returned from his wanderings to begin his scientific career at St. Thomas's Hospital. At thirty-six he became a Fellow of the Royal Society and at thirty-eight Holt Professor of Physiology at Liverpool; and, finally, to Oxford at fifty-six.

When Sherrington arrived in Oxford, Osler was Regius Professor of Medicine. Both men collected books; Osler, in a big way, was gathering a historical library which he was to leave to McGill University, and Sherrington, in a smaller way, was collecting the books of special interest to him, some of which he gave to the Medical Library of the University of British Columbia.

William Francis, now Curator of the Osler Library at McGill, records an amusing bookish misadventure. Here is the version I had from him. In 1915, Sir Charles lent Sir William one of his rare possessions, acquired when he was at Caius College, a first edition of Descartes' *De Homine*. Some time later, while visiting the Osler home, Sherrington saw his volume on a shelf and, taking it down, unobserved, he read on the fly-leaf in Osler's hand, "Given to me by my colleague Sherrington." He took out his pen and wrote above the Oslerian inscription: "Guglielmo Osler per Car. Sherrington", and dated it 1917. Thus he converted the intended loan into a gift, without mentioning it to anyone. No one knew until Francis came to catalogue the Osler library ten years later, long after Osler's death. Sherrington then confessed his gift-by-stealth with a twinkle in his eye, and refused to take back the once cherished possession.

Throughout the world this year, many will look back on the career of this man, born in London on November 27, 1857. It is clear that his physiological and philosophical teachings will live on, but for most people Sherrington the man is no more than a legend. Even those who have met him may well remember only that he was a shy man with a small body and a preoccupied manner; a man oblivious of his own great stature and reputation.

For me he is much more than a legend. He was my teacher and he is still my scientific hero. When I went to Oxford as an undergraduate I met him for the first time. He was fifty-seven years old then, a quick-moving man of medium height with a small moustache and nose-glasses, who hurried along the corridors in a white coat, or moved from table to table while we worked on our "preparations." How well I remember him peering, short-sighted, over my embarrassed shoulder. His face was smooth and almost expressionless, but I watched for the faint smile and the twinkle of humour and understanding in his eyes. "Hm, Penfield, you may be right," he would say, "but, I should have thought . . . "

Then he would pick up the delicately pointed forceps and change the tissues of the preparation so as to set the youthful experimenter back on "the right track." Sherrington seemed quite sincere in the expectation that each student would teach him something, some time.

He lectured to us using copious headings and subheadings which he chalked on the board before the members of the class assembled. He presented us with both sides of each physiological problem, sometimes leaving his hearers in a state of frustrated confusion. The undergraduate usually prefers brief and positive statements of the "facts" made by a professor who hides his doubts beneath a mantle of shining authority. It gives the student such a sense of security, especially in regard to examinations.

In later years, when I returned to Oxford for graduate study, and during recurrent visits with him through the long period of his retirement, I came to appreciate the brilliant mind and the broad culture of this modest seeker after the truth. Harvey Cushing was an observer of Sherrington's work in Liverpool for a time, though never a regular worker in his laboratory. He reported the Professor to be a man in a hurry who wrote too much and had a poor memory for many things including his glasses. This is a curiously superficial misconception on the part of the great American neurosurgeon!

I would say from my long acquaintance with him that Sherrington's memory excelled that of any man I have ever known, for accuracy of detail, whether employed in the telling of thrilling tales of his adventurous youth, or in the recollection of scientific detail. At dinner in the hall of Magdalen College he would discuss literature, history, art, life – according to the wit and interest of his companions – and quietly excel in every field.

He retired from the Chair of Physiology at Oxford in 1936. According to present university regulations, he would have been forced to retire at sixty-five, in 1922. He was knighted that year, 1922, and received the Order of Merit two years later. The scientific work of the extra fourteen years was carried out with younger men such as T. Liddell, R. S. Creed, S. Cooper, D. E. Denny-Brown, J. C. Eccles, J. F. Fulton – sound work and of great value. Liddell, who succeeded him as professor at Oxford, has described that happy time as "a busy and fruitful autumn of scientific endeavour, in which much of his earlier work came to full harvest."

During that period he became President of the Royal Society and Editor of the *Journal of Physiology*. He travelled to Harvard to give the Dunham Lectures and honours came fast, capped by the award of the Nobel Prize which he shared in 1932 with Professor (now Lord) Adrian.

But, although the scientific work of this period was a fulfilment of his earlier research, there was a beginning of contribution in other fields. His collected poems appeared, in first edition, under the title: "The Assaying of Brabantius" in 1925. He turned to philosophical thinking in his Rede Lecture in 1933.

Following formal retirement he was called upon immediately to deliver the Gifford Lectures at Edinburgh University, 1937 – 38. According to the terms of that lectureship, he was expected to throw light on what Lord Gifford called "Natural Theology." At about the time of retirement, as I have mentioned, he seems to have discovered Jean Fernel, a French physiologist, whose philosophical thought he was to describe in a later book as *The Endeavour of Jean Fernel* (1946), venturing thus into biography. The Gifford Lectures appeared under the title, *Man On His Nature* (1940). This book has proved popular with readers in different disciplines everywhere. It has actually come to a paper edition and, through it, into the hands of a multitude.

Thus it came about that Sir Charles Sherrington turned from cat and chimpanzee to man. The biologist became a philosopher and approached the problem that lies forever between them. To be more exact, the biologist turned his attention to the philosophical implications of neurophysiology. He addressed himself to the mind-body relationship.

In the Gifford Lectures, he considered it first from a historical point of view. The era of scientific inquiry into this field of speculation began, he said, with the work of Galvani. Soon it was evident that nerves conducted energy to muscles. This led directly to discovery of the astounding secrets of electricity. So it was, Sherrington wrote, that "transient electrical potentials travelling the fibres of the nervous system" replaced the spirits of the anima in the understanding of scientists, if not in the speech of the man in the street.

In time, and I quote his words, "knowledge looking at its world had painfully, and not without some disillusions, arrived at two concepts; the one, that of energy which was adequate to deal with all which was known to knowledge, except mind. But between energy and mind science found no 'how' of give and take. There was co-existence; that was all. To man's understanding the world remained obstinately double."

In 1950, two years before Sherrington's death, at a special meeting of the U.S.S.R. Academy of Science, Ivan Pavlov was held up as a leader of the monist point of view and his work on conditioned reflexes cited as proof of the validity of the philosophy of materialism. Sherrington, on the other hand, was viewed by these scientists as the great dualist in physiology. But both men, in their physiological work, had studied and recorded the phenomena of nature objectively, as good scientists should. They had analysed neurological mechanisms and recorded concomitant changes of behaviour. We do wrong to make them leaders or adherents of schools of philosophical conviction.

In physiology Sherrington was a realist, a scientist seeking truth without bias. The conclusions of his philosophical thinking and the question of what his own faith may have been should never be confused with his work as a scientist.

One of his distinguished American pupils, Stanley Cobb, hailed him as the outstanding proponent of dualism after Socrates and Descartes, meaning, I suppose, that he believed that the existence of two separate elements, the body and spirit, was established. In his Rede Lecture, Sherrington had pondered this question. "It will long offer," he said, "to those who pursue it, the comfort that to journey is better than to arrive; but that comfort assumes arrival. Some of us, perhaps because we are too old – or is it too young – think there may be arrival at last."

He had faith, this old man who was forever young, that success would come to physiology in time, and understanding to scientist and philosopher alike. But he turned from the problem that neither could solve, to see life with the eyes of a poet.

The night is fallen and still thou speakst to me,
what though with one voice sole, with accents many,
tongued turret and tongued stream, tracked pasture fenny
and cloister spirit-trod, and centuried tree.

Nature spoke to him with many tongues and with accents many. He understood her accents and could integrate them in his thinking until he seemed at last to comprehend the meaning of life, the design of the Creator.

* * *

Sir Charles Sherrington, O.M., G.B.E., F.R.S., died in 1952 at the age of ninety-five. In his heyday, he had been the world's foremost neurophysiologist. After my years of graduate study with him, he continued to influence my scientific thinking more profoundly than anyone else. And yet I have made scant reference to his scientific thought. Instead I have tried to picture the man as he was in leisure time, and describe the other careers of a scientific genius.

Ramón y Cajal

[EIGHT]

*It has been said many a time that the problem
of Spain is a problem of culture. It is necessary
in fact, if we would enrol ourselves with the
civilized peoples, that we cultivate intensively
the deserts of our land and brain, thus rescuing
by prosperity and mental vigour all those
national riches that have been lost in the sea
and all those talents which have been lost in
ignorance.*

These words were scrawled in Spanish across the portrait of
Ramón y Cajal. I had been conscious of keen eyes looking down
from that portrait during my first day of work in the laboratory
of Pio del Rio-Hortega, and finally stopped to decipher the
scrawl. Before coming to Spain in 1924 I had learned much
about Cajal, that great master of the Spanish school of neurology, from his scientific publications. But the writer of these
words must be more than a closeted scientist; a critic, a prophet
perhaps, certainly a master of literary style.

In America it had been rather difficult to explain how one
could profitably spend six months in Spain learning new
methods of medical research. But here in Madrid, Cajal, winner
of the Nobel Prize, was a figure much talked about though
rarely seen. His name seemed to be a password, for had we not
obtained entrance into a pension heretofore restricted to
Spaniards by mentioning that I had come to work under the
great scientist? In like manner did we not secure the little pisa

FIRST PUBLISHED IN 1926.

for a permanent residence? The magic of his name made introductions easy and conversations immediately absorbing and
satisfactory to the Spaniard, who welcomes above all else a
tribute from abroad to the culture and intellectual distinction
of his race.

In university and scientific circles Don Santiago, as he was
called, seemed to be a sort of dean and censor; to educational
reformers a much needed ally, and in politics a figure whose
power was recognized even by the Dictator Primo Rivera. The
peasant and the townsman understood nothing of his scientific
work. It was enough for them that from foreign lands came
prizes and homage to this son of Spain, that he exhorted them
to the stern virtues of their great ancestors and was himself a
sign of the return of greatness to their land.

My first meeting with Cajal made a deep impression on me.
It was in the library of his laboratory, and I found him sitting
as though in dejection, with head fallen forward on his chest
so that only white hair and beard could be seen. His long arms
hung down almost to the floor. As I hesitated in the doorway
he started up and came forward with the graceful courtesy common to his race. With quick comprehension in his dark eyes he
welcomed me as a foreign pilgrim to the laboratory and spoke
of his great desire that the outside world should know of the
achievements of the little group of scientists about him.

Placing his hand on a shelf that held his own publications
and those of his pupils, most of them in Spanish, he said with
much feeling in his voice, "These books are unknown abroad.
Scientists will not read Spanish. Almost every week I learn
from German or American journals that men are rediscovering
what I did long ago." With increasing agitation he expressed
his fear that the Spanish school of neurology would be ignored
and disappear after his death. Then with an abrupt change of
manner he took my arm and added, "Let me show you the
laboratory and I have here some photomicrographs in colour
which you will like to see." This first interview roused a desire
to know more about the man – a desire easily satisfied, for his
admirers were glad to talk, and there were his popular writings
and autobiography.

Cajal, Spain's first great scientist, was a man whose genius may be compared with that of Pasteur. He came, like Pasteur, from the people and developed spontaneously in his native land. When he was born in 1852, in the pueblo of Petilla, his father, Ramón y Cassasus, was practising surgery among the poor peasants of the Pyrenees.

This pueblo, situated high on a treeless mountain, was connected with the outside world by a footpath only wide enough for man or donkey. The elder Ramón, who had caught from some long-dead Aragonese ancestor a spark of restless ambition, had earned the degree of "Surgeon of the Second Class" under the most difficult circumstances. But not satisfied with that, he aspired to the more glorious distinction of a Diploma in Medicine, and, as a result of determined application to his mountain practice and the rigid economy of his household, he was able to come down from the Pyrenees, complete his medical education and finally bring his ever growing family to live in the university town of Zaragoza.

Thus the elder Ramón rose from his peasant home to a respectable professional position and a professorship in the university. He taught the boy Santiago to read French and, finding him quick to learn, determined that he should receive a medical education. Young Ramón, however, seemed to have inherited, in addition to his father's restless spirit, a talent for art. Doutbless this love of painting was quite natural, since he came from a race which has yielded so many great artists and lived in a country where interest in art is so prevalent.

His career in school was not brilliant. Too much of his time was spent in drawing and painting. An artist who came to decorate the church of the village in which the Ramóns were living at that time declared that the products of young Santiago's brush had no merit. However, some of his drawings done at the age of eight have been preserved and it seems quite likely that members of the more realistic modern school of art would have found promise in them. At any rate, the artist's verdict confirmed his father's decision that the boy was to become a doctor of medicine, and away to the School of Catholic Fathers he was sent, to learn Latin. The schoolmasters found him indifferent and told him that he had no memory, a pronouncement he readily believed, like many another mistaught pupil.

The parent was puzzled, other schools were tried, and on two occasions he was removed from school altogether. At the first removal he was apprenticed to a barber, so that in case medicine failed, he should at least have a trade at which to earn an honest living. Perhaps the elder Ramón felt that as the barber is ancestor to the surgeon, the boy might somehow pass from hair-cutting to surgery. The second time his school career was interrupted Santiago was apprenticed to a cobbler, for whose trade he showed so much aptitude that, at the end of the year, the cobbler desired him to sign for a long period.

There were illicit schoolday enthusiasms in addition to art. One was an absorbing interest in the habits of birds, and another developed after he stumbled on a library of novels. *Don Quixote* and *Robinson Crusoe* seem to have been his favourites, and this admiration resulted in the writing of his first book, which was patterned after Crusoe's adventures.

Eventually, the despairing parent determined to take matters into his own hands. He himself undertook to teach the boy osteology, which he considered the cornerstone of medicine; and Cajal began dutifully to read about bones. But textbook pictures did not satisfy this student. He wanted to see things for himself. And so he made a moonlit journey to the burying-ground, and braving the awful creatures of his imagination, he bore away the coveted models in terrified haste to an old granary. The granary became the classroom, and here father and son studied bones; and the boy at last found inclination and duty running parallel. The artist in him discovered an approved outlet, and he made pictures of bones large and small from every angle. Like Leonardo da Vinci he found a joy in drawing the component parts as great as that in reproducing the integrated living body; and like Leonardo he became a skilled anatomist.

When the family made their last move, to the capital of Aragon, the elder Ramón was appointed professor of anatomy in the University of Zaragoza and the son was among his first pupils. The study of anatomy was continued for three years, and the new professor planned the publication of an atlas of anatomy based on his son's brilliant drawings. But this plan was never realized because of the impossibility of securing good reproductions.

Absorbing hobbies played an important part in Cajal's life from the start. During his university career he became the prey of a number of them. One of the most surprising was a mania for gymnastics. On discovering that an acquaintance had stronger wrists than he, he inquired and found that his adversary exercised habitually. Thereupon, young Cajal asserted that within six months he would excel this new-found rival. He immediately plunged into an intensive course of gymnastics to which he devoted two hours daily. After exhausting all the prescribed exercises he devised new ones, and not only vanquished his rival in less than six months but also became the champion strong man of the university gymnasium.

He observed later that the possession of such superlative strength made him long to exert it and humorously told the following tale. Among the university students at that time a certain young lady of the town was much celebrated for beauty of face and form. She was called "Venus de Milo" for no one had met her, and her true name was unknown. But of an evening she could be seen sitting on the balcony of her home, and Cajal often passed through that street in the hope of seeing her. One evening, when following his usual path homeward, he was accosted by another admirer who informed him that in the future he was to avoid this street. Cajal recognized the man as a student of the engineering school, a youth famed for physical prowess. Every muscle fibre in Cajal's sturdy body cried out for joy at the prospect of a struggle, and the two sought a secluded field of combat. First honours appear to have gone to the engineer, as he struck Cajal several mighty blows on the head with his stick, which made it impossible for him to wear a hat for days. At any rate the tide of battle turned and the young medical student encircled his opponent's chest in a mighty hug. Tightening his huge arms, he watched for the physiological effect. There was not long to wait. The face of his adversary became livid, and he slipped unconscious to the ground. Horrified at the thought that he might have done him some irremediable harm, Cajal revived his fallen rival, helped him to dress and assisted him to his lodgings. But it seems the beautiful "Venus de Milo" was not destined for either of them. She was carried off by envious microbes, a victim to tuberculosis.

In looking back at that period Cajal later remarked that his aptitude for intellectual work decreased rapidly. The brain, he said, fatigued by its motor discharges apparently loses capacity for associative activity. The structural differentiation of the central nervous system seems to be suspended and activity of the higher centres superseded by that of the centres devoted to muscular control. This compensatory process, he felt, explains why the youths who excel physically are, with certain exceptions, not talkers and "possess a poor and rude intellect." However, he was prevented from becoming a victim of his athleticism by a severe attack of malaria acquired in Cuba. This, together with a subsequent almost fatal attack of pulmonary tuberculosis, relieved his cerebral grey matter of its burden of excess muscle.

Military service in Cuba followed the completion of his medical studies, and on returning to Spain he was appointed assistant in anatomy on the faculty of the University of Zaragoza. He then went to Madrid to be examined for his doctorate, and there for the first time he saw a microscope. His interest was immediately aroused, and he spent the savings that had accumulated during his long illness in Cuba to buy a microtome, a few books and a good German microscope, the first in the University of Zaragoza. From the books he learned how to make microscopic sections and began alone his study of the "infinitely small."

Several years later he won the contest for the professorship of anatomy at the university of Valencia and there, at the age of thirty-two, he fitted up a little laboratory in his home and eked out his meagre salary by coaching graduate students. There he began in earnest the work of investigation that was to add so much to our knowledge of the nervous system.

Scientific investigation was a thing quite foreign to the culture of Spaniards. They have always been a people passionately proud of their former greatness, of the splendour that once was Spain's. They continue even now to be conscious of a superiority, the material proof of which vanished three hundred years ago with the loss of the treasure found in America. Art and literature were sanctioned by the past and might deal with approved pious subjects. Spaniards might be original in literature and might speak with authority on art, but originality in science was unheard of at that time.

Nevertheless, Cajal began to publish what he saw under his microscope, at first modestly in Spain. Then he determined that to become strong he must struggle against the strong, and he began sending communications to foreign journals. He was looked on with suspicion by his friends. A query ran among the faculty, "Who is this Cajal to pass judgment on foreign authorities?" He began to use silver to stain the finest cellular elements after the method of the great Italian, Golgi. As he applied this method with certain practical modifications of his own to the study of the brain, the intricate structure of nerve cells began to unfold before his eyes. Not having means to employ an illustrator he drew what his microscope showed him and illustrated his own papers. Here were problems worthy of his greatest effort and Cajal responded with a furious enthusiasm that never flagged.

He soon observed that foreign workers either ignored his contributions or treated them lightly. He therefore determined to demonstrate his preparations before the German Society of Anatomists. In Berlin, he found the members of that society sceptical about his work, rather than curious to see it. But he also saw this attitude change after they had examined his beautiful specimens and had seen the nerve cells of the cerebellum as never before, the ascending and descending branches of sensory cells and the termination of the retinal fibres in the optic lobes. That he had scored a triumph in spite of the odds he knew, when Kölliker, the patriarch of German histology, came to him at the close of the conference to praise his work in the highest terms. Before returning to Spain he went to visit numerous German laboratories and discovered, to his surprise, that some of the most justly famous were provided not with good equipment but only with men whose enthusiasm resembled his own.

In 1892, Cajal moved to Madrid with his family to take a professorship in that university. Here he found congenial friends, and in spite of habitual application to his laboratory, he maintained many other interests. He was fond of walks into the open country about Madrid and thought the greys and yellows, the browns and blues of the bare Castilian plain, far lovelier than the unchanging wet green of northern countries. His camera was ever in use on these excursions, and he prepared his own plates for colour photographs. Also, after the invariable Spanish custom, he was to be found daily at a certain café in the company of congenial friends who held their "tertulia" there. Over their coffee cups they talked or played chess, and Cajal forgot the problems of the laboratory and gave himself up to a "diastole of rest" in preparation for the day's "systole of work." Yet his mind, even in periods of rest, was creative, and his diastolic reflections found eventual expression in a charming book called *Coffee House Chatter*, just as the hobby of leisure moments gave birth to a book on colour photography.

His scientific publications increased in volume and importance. He elaborated important work on the retina and olfactory lobes and fought for the individuality of nerve cells against the exponents of the reticular theory. Cajal believed in working ever with a guiding hypothesis, although such hypotheses, he said, fall into oblivion, except for those parts of them which are susceptible of scientific proof. He passed beyond the field of simple structure into theories of the mechanism of thought, association of ideas, and attention.

There came an invitation from the Royal Society of London to deliver the Croonian Lecture, perhaps the highest honour he could receive from the English capital. With it was a cordial invitation from Charles Sherrington, already the most brilliant physiologist of England, offering him the hospitality of his home. That lectureship and the honorary degrees received from Oxford and Cambridge were a real triumph for any scientist, and an unheard-of thing for a Spaniard.

The visit of this brilliant and eccentric scientist from Spain made a deep impression on scientific London and it was made a feature in the political life of the day. It is told that, during the first week of his stay in the home of Sir Charles Sherrington, Cajal carefully kept the key to his bedchamber with him, saying that he preferred to care for the room himself, but when his hostess finally gained access to the room she found that it had come to look more like a laboratory than a bedroom. There were bottles in the windows, on the chairs and on the floor, perhaps the apparatus of some experiment whose answer he could not wait to know.

When he went from London to Cambridge to receive a degree, a special effort was made to get him to the London station in plenty of time. This too great zeal resulted in his taking an earlier train than the one he was intended to take, so that no one met him at the station in Cambridge. Long after the luncheon which had been prepared in his honour was finished, he was found wandering through the colleges admiring their beauty, unconscious of the consternation that had arisen in the breast of his would-be host.

Recognition of his scientific eminence followed rapidly from other countries. The year after the Spanish-American war, Cajal was invited to lecture in the United States at Clark University. It was July when he arrived in New York, the city known in Spain for "its skyscrapers, its avaricious trusts and its heat." He was astonished at the "stern fibre of the Anglo-Saxon race" which impelled even labourers to activity under such a blazing sun. He seemed much interested in American home life and democracy, but he was a little taken aback to see a college professor shoulder his trunk at the station, and when that energetic educator told him that manual labour was considered an obligation in this land of democracy, he observed dryly that he perceived that the abolition of aristocrats was not sufficient to achieve democracy – it was also necessary to develop muscles of steel! Señora Cajal, who accompanied him, looked with disapproving surprise on the new American woman who at that time was bursting into feminism, disapproval which her husband seems to have shared.

Distinctions rained on Cajal. The International Medical Congress Medal of 1903 was awarded him and this congress met that year in Madrid for the first time. There followed the Helmholtz and Nobel prizes. These crowning awards were the occasion for felicitations from all over Spain, and Cajal received great ovations from the press, his own countrymen being the last to recognize the value of his work. But in Cajal such things produced a curious mental depression, and he turned with stern determination to attack the problems that lurked beneath his microscope.

When I knew him, Cajal still worked in his laboratory, carrying his seventy-odd years lightly. The old enthusiasm for research still burned within him, though his capacity for sustained effort had decreased. At times he was a little bitter when he saw the scientific world ignoring his past work, and he began to publish the laboratory communications in French in the hope that the voices of his pupils might be less often ignored than his own had been.

Foreign students never seem to have found their way to Cajal's laboratory. The barriers of language and of custom turned medical men to other countries, and Spain seemed out of the current of scientific advance. But there was much more than science to be learned from Don Santiago if you sought him out in the little café on the corner. There he was wont to sit over his coffee and muse on many things as he watched the changing currents of modern Spain flow through the Plaza de Atocha.

Surgery and Science

"There is a river not to be found on any map of this terrestrial globe, yet a river well known to all the sons of men, and never very far from any of us. It flows in the Realm of Time. It is Lethe, the river of Oblivion. What memories of noble persons and heroic deeds, what words of wisdom and what glorious thoughts have been engulfed in that dark, remorseless tide!

"To retrieve, if it may be, from its 'watery labyrinth' and to preserve something of the character, the appearance, the thought and speech, the little unremembered acts of our heroes and benefactors, as well as to keep bright the story of their life work, is the object of such orations as this –"

These are not my words. Do not be so far encouraged. These words which, by their beauty, will survive the "dark remorseless tide" of oblivion, were the words of John Stewart. These were his thoughts in his introduction to the first Listerian Oration before the Canadian Medical Association at Ottawa in 1924. In my turn, I shall do my best to recall to you something of the character and thought of Dr. John Stewart and of his friend and master Lord Lister, for he who would recall the one recalls the other.

There could be no better introduction to a consideration of the relationship of Surgery and Science. These men may have drunk the waters of oblivion for themselves according to the Greek myth. We in this world cannot know that for certain. But, for us, they constitute a legend of growing power. In giving this lecture I wear the mantle of Stewart proudly for a little time, here in the city that he loved and before friends who have

FROM THE JOHN STEWART MEMORIAL LECTURE, DALHOUSIE UNIVERSITY, HALIFAX; OCTOBER 1953.

not forgotten him. He served this university well as Professor of Surgery and as Dean. There are, no doubt, many patients who remember him, and many colleagues who could speak of him with greater authority than I.

When Lister left Edinburgh to accept the chair of surgery at King's College Hospital, London, he took with him his house surgeon, W. Watson Cheyne, and his senior clerk, John Stewart. Sir St. Clair Thompson was an undergraduate medical student at King's at the time and he has given us the following description of the two young men.

"They were, each in his way, typical specimens of two races which are found in Scotland north of the Grampians. Watson Cheyne with his red hair and honey-coloured beard showed the Scandinavian origin of the inhabitants of Shetland. . . . Stewart was a splendid specimen of the black-haired Highlander: tall, stalwart, handsome, dignified, gracious, with courtly manners and soft clear speech."

Fraser-Harris has said that Stewart's admiration for Lister almost amounted to worship. "The Quaker and the Highlander," he pointed out, "were cast in the same mould, for both were conscientious, intellectually honest, reverent and deeply religious."

There the identity stops. Stewart was a disciple. His contribution to our profession consisted in his advocacy and his practice of the new gospel, the introduction of antisepsis in surgery. Stewart returned home, to the seaport town of Pictou. Perhaps one might marvel that he returned as he did, leaving behind him the wards and the laboratories, the experimentation, the discussions and the doubts of Edinburgh and London.

Pictou in 1879 was a proud little town. It seemed to turn its back on the rest of Canada that sprawled in new-formed union across the continent. Quebec, Ontario, Manitoba, British Columbia! Their problems seemed foreign in Pictou, and Confederation futile. Even New Brunswick was far away. Pictou looked out over the sea, in the direction of the sunrise, toward old Scotland. It was not far off. The town might have been in the Hebrides instead of on another continent for all the notice it took of the distance. It was Old Scotland and New Scotland and there was one people and Edinburgh and Halifax were two highland capitals.

Stewart practised surgery in Pictou. He took an interest in the lives and the pastimes of his people and remained there fifteen years. Then, coming to Halifax, he became the perfect teacher, the admirable example, the beloved practitioner. He was a scholar, a gentleman, an excellent surgeon. Having listened to a voice of authority he undertook the care of the sick. The practitioner is the flower of our profession.

The difference between Stewart and Lister, two men said to be cast by nature in the same mould, is that the one accepted authority and went to work among his people. The other doubted as he worked and put his doubts to the test again and again. – Surgery for the one and surgery with the pursuit of science for the other.

What was it that made Lister a scientist as well as a surgeon? Let us look for the answer in the story of his early life.

On graduating in medicine from University College, London, Lister became house surgeon to Ericksen, author of the most popular current textbook of surgery. The book was called, hopefully, *Science and the Art of Surgery*. But Ericksen was not a scientist according to my definition.

Young Lister passed his F.R.C.S. examinations at the age of twenty-five and so was qualified for his practice. There had been prizes. It was all very proper and highly satisfactory. The time had come for him to tour the clinics of the Continent, to take his wander year, before setting up as a London surgeon. He had money enough to do as he liked.

But Lister was depressed. He looked at the surgical wards – what a lottery of life and death! Infection dogged the surgeon's every incision and seemed to leap from bed to bed. He turned back to the laboratories of University College, to William Sharpey. Sharpey was a scientist, not a surgeon. He concerned himself with basic mechanisms in medicine. His pupil Michael Foster writing years later said of him that he was, at the time of Lister's student days, the only pure physiologist in England.

Sharpey was a Scot and he suggested to his young and discontented pupil that he go to Scotland to visit Syme who was then Professor of Surgery at Edinburgh and an old friend of Sharpey's. Syme was honest, his words few, his surgery unexcelled for that period. So, Lister went for a month's visit, but he remained seven years, beginning all over again as Syme's house surgeon (and eventually marrying his daughter!).

This tall, thoughtful young man was somehow different. He had known culture as a boy. His father, Joseph Jackson Lister, although a wine merchant from the age of fourteen when he had to leave school, had "contrived, by early rising and otherwise, to supplement the school education." He eventually did work of great value on the theory and construction of achromatic lenses for microscopes. Indeed, because of this, he became in his own right a Fellow of the Royal Society.

The son Joseph had a boyhood desire to become a surgeon. But his father, recognizing like many another father the value of what he himself had missed, sent him for a preliminary course in arts to University College, three years leading to the degree of B.A., before he should undertake the study of medicine. Lord Lister, in later life, was in the habit of advising this for young men who were considering medicine and who could find the time and money.

But at the close of his study of arts there came an unplanned interlude. He seemed to have a depression. It was called a "nervous breakdown" then as it is now. And so he was given an extended holiday in Ireland; a place of beauty that was reasonably free of intellectual distraction, a place to relax – where a man might laugh and not be asked the reason for it.

Joseph Jackson's letter written to his son at this time, with its Quaker intimacy, gives insight into the son's state of mind:

"It is indeed a mistake . . . to believe thyself required to bear burthens on account of the states of others . . . and believe us, my tenderly beloved son, that the proper part now is to cherish a pious cheerful spirit, open to see and to enjoy the bounties and beauties spread around us – not to give way to turning thy thoughts upon thyself, nor even at present to dwell long on serious things. Thou wilt remember how strongly Dr. Hodgkin cautioned thee on these points."*

Thus although he had his B.A. at twenty, Lister did not begin

---

* Sir Rickman Godlee, *Lord Lister* (London: Macmillan, 1917) , p. 16. Godlee, who was Lister's nephew, himself made history when he was the first to carry out a temporarily successful operation for brain tumour at Queen Square in 1884.

medical studies until he was twenty-one. He had had a year for reading and reflection, time to doubt his own abilities and to look at life. Such periods may profoundly alter character. Edward Archibald, McGill University's greatest surgeon, had such a period of nearly two years during a cure for pulmonary tuberculosis. When he returned to surgery he had, as I think in consequence, a unique turn of mind. He was reflective, perceptive, different. One of the whimsical sprites that are only found in silent places had crept into his mind. An even more dramatic change was wrought in William Halsted by a similar period, as I shall describe later.

Lister had a tendency to stutter, particularly when tired or embarrassed. His hands, as pointed out apologetically by his biographer, were not long and beautiful like his mother's – hands thought then, and since, to be clever and artistic. On the contrary, Lister's hands were square and thick and the fingers short, like those of many an expert carpenter and artisan, the hands of Hunter and Kocher and Halsted and Finney and Cushing.

Being more mature than his classmates, Lister, even before he left medical school, turned his attention to original work in basic science. In physiology, his earliest writings had to do with muscle histology, blood vessels, circulation, nervous control of blood vessels, coagulation of the blood. In the field of pathology and bacteriology, he contributed original work on inflammation, and eventually the new germ theory.

He was not interested, as many surgeons are, in making large collections of pathological specimens. How different he was from John Hunter in this respect! He did not begin by publishing a long series of cases in which the patients had been treated in a standard manner. Instead he published one case of bony exostosis removed by Syme from the humerus of a young girl, analysing the formation of cartilage and the biological mechanism of laying down bone in it. He reported a single case of carbuncle from the practice of Professor Syme. Think of it – one carbuncle! But he took it as a text for an inquiry into the pathology of infection and inflammation.

In 1860 at thirty-three years of age he was made a Fellow of the Royal Society, not as a recognition of his distinction as an assistant surgeon, but because of his original work in the biological sciences that are basic to surgery. He chose the unsolved problems that the practice of surgery had presented to his mind.

In the same year he left Edinburgh to accept the chair of the Regius Professor of Surgery in Glasgow.

At thirty-eight he conceived the true explanation of sepsis and devised a method of treatment called antisepsis.

During those seven years in the clinic of Syme at Edinburgh and the succeeding five years in Glasgow, before he picked up the clue to his great discovery, he was a busy surgeon like other surgeons. But he was something more, a scientist. He was a scientist by virtue of his habit of thought.

He turned from the patient to current medical literature and back to the patient. But he did not accept the pronouncements and the explanations of the surgeons and physicians about him, or who had gone before him, without critical consideration of the evidence. He recognized no authority of name or position.

Instead he looked at clinical problems with the eye of one who has himself done original work on microscopic structure and who has made his own inquiry into living mechanisms. He went from the patient to his simplified laboratory experiments and back again, seeking cause and effect. He depended on those things that could be proven. Thus his thinking about clinical problems was scientific rather than authoritarian.

Here is the crux of the whole problem. When he looked at an osteoma he recalled the growth of cartilage and the change to bone that he had seen with his own eyes. The element of cause of local tumour growth he must have recognized as a continuing mystery. That element remains a mystery to us today while we wait for someone to pick up a clue, perhaps from new work in some other discipline of science. We are waiting for a Lister in the field of cancer, for the evolution of Science in Surgery.

He looked at a carbuncle, understanding the swelling, the redness, the central disintegration of tissue, in terms of his own basic observations of inflammation and structure and circulation. He was clear about one thing – namely that the ultimate causal agent was unknown and current surgical reasoning was wrong.

I like to think that he took a special interest in Pasteur's work on putrefaction in wine because of his affection for his own father the wine merchant. Pasteur at that time had seemed to destroy minute organisms in the wine by heat. Lister knew he could not use heat in surgery. That would kill his patient. Sepsis in a wound resembled putrefaction. There must be micro-organisms at the bottom of the process.

He thought long about the problem. He tried zinc chloride, also sulphites, but without success. Then an item of apparently unrelated information came to him. The city of Carlisle was using carbolic acid to combat putrefaction in sewage. That must have seemed a far cry from the operating room but his scientific mind had narrowed the problem down to a search for something that would kill a hypothetical living organism without killing the patient. Other clinicians still believed in spontaneous generation of life, and they taught it. But Lister found their proofs inconclusive!

Pasteur had shown that micro-organisms could reach his cultures through the air. And so it was that Lister converted carbolic acid solution into a vapour to cleanse the air about the wound as well as the wound. The scheme succeeded and so it was that antisepsis won the first round against infection.

We realize now that Lister's discovery was only a step. It is always so in science – a step toward the whole truth and the final solution.

Aseptic techniques were to follow, associated with antiseptic sterilization of the skin. A little later, at the time of the first world war, wounds were again to be treated with antiseptics such as the hypochlorite solution of Dakin. Still later the antibiotics were to appear, destroying micro-organisms selectively on the basis of a new principle, without harm to the patient.

At least two surgeons who preceded Lister may be compared with him because of the value of their contributions: Ambroise Paré in the sixteenth century and John Hunter in the eighteenth. Neither of these men had any such primary scientific training as Lister. It was far too early for that to have been possible. But both men were like him in one regard. They refused to accept traditional teaching as final authority, preferring to turn to nature itself for evidence.

Paré was a country barber's apprentice who acquired some experience as a dresser in the Hôtel Dieu de Paris. He became an army surgeon without passing through the medical schools of the period and, after long and trying experiences on the battlefields of France, he came to defy tradition in the treatment of wounds. He was guided by fearless compassion for the suffering of his patients, and by practical experiment. Thus it was that he established better methods of treatment and forbade gratuitous interference, enunciating the principle that God would heal if the surgeon provided care and protective dressings.

Paré was a magnificent technician, devising many splints and new procedures. He was beloved by the people and yet treated with contempt by established physicians of his time. Paré was the only "Protestant" to be spared by royal mandate at the massacre of St. Bartholomew. But he was a protestant in medicine as well as in religion.

John Hunter was born in 1728, a hundred years before Lister. He has been called, with good reason, the founder of scientific surgery.

Hunter was a surgeon, an experimentalist, a collector of everything that had to do with his changing interest in the human body. The thirteen thousand specimens which he gathered together and studied were passed on to the Royal College of Surgeons and I am myself convinced that his restless iconoclastic spirit still lurks in the Hunterian museum. When at the College in Lincoln's Inn Fields, I think I have heard his cynical laughter as students walk through the collection with books in hand peering about to see the things that the textbooks say they should see.

He was tireless, irascible, intolerant, lovable, fervent. He seemed to be born with the urge of a collector, but he turned from his collecting with apparently inexhaustible energy to put the questions that presented themselves to the experimental test. Experimentation also seems to have been, in him, an inborn turn of mind. All knowledge in the field of surgical pathology was his goal but he took the body of man and the bodies of animals living and dead as the text for his authority.

No man was ever less bound by the teaching of the past. Indeed he was, to a large extent, unhampered by traditional teaching because he seemed to be ignorant of it! He did not come to surgery with a mind trained by study of basic science, as Lister did. Instead he came to anatomy and to surgery with a critical and inquiring mind to assemble a body of facts which formed the beginning of surgical pathology. He showed surgeons that each of them, whatever his training, might contribute to this science, provided he continued to look for final authority in the structure of the body and in the experiments wrought there by disease.

I could choose many examples. But I shall only refer to one more master surgeon, William Stewart Halsted. He is perhaps the only man to have founded a school of surgery on this continent unless such a claim could be made for Harvey Cushing. But Cushing, in a very real sense, was Halsted's pupil.

Halsted was Professor of Surgery at Johns Hopkins for thirty-three years from the foundation of its Medical School in 1889. He taught his pupils a new delicacy in the handling of tissue, introduced the use of rubber gloves in the operating room and gave an example of thoughtful scholarship in his approach to surgical problems that has had a profound effect on American surgeons.

A tragedy and a period of enforced reflection changed him as a young man and made of him the shy studious Professor I knew when I was an undergraduate at the Johns Hopkins. As a young man, Halsted returned from study in Germany to the thundering turmoil of New York, the most urban and in many ways the most challenging city of the world. He was hailed as a rapid, brilliant operator, a popular teacher, a promising surgeon in the best tradition of New York's Roosevelt Hospital.

Then there came upon him the tragic addiction to cocaine, long guarded as a secret by his friends. It had been acquired while testing the newly discovered drug upon himself before the dangers of habituation were understood. The result was a gradually increasing confusion of thought that for a time puzzled all who knew him. An unworthy medical article appeared under his name at that time which bears testimony to his strange mental breakdown. His close friend, the pathologist William Welch, recognized the cause of the trouble and came to his rescue.

Together they went off on a long sea voyage to the Windward Islands and back. It was heroic treatment in that tiny schooner. There followed nine months of seclusion in the Butler Hospital, and then at last Halsted emerged – cured but changed. There was a transitional period in Welch's Laboratory. Then he took over the Department of Surgery as Osler did the Department of Medicine.

The tragedy and the period of solitude made him different. We might all of us do more meaningful work, make more strategic approach to problems, if we turned aside to seek a distant perspective.

I have talked about the heroes of our profession, and the relationship of science to surgery. Science for a physician is the same as science for a surgeon, with no more than a change in emphasis. Few can make such a successful adjustment between surgery and science as Joseph Lister did. Many have not had the advantage of preliminary training in the arts. Many could not indulge in the long period of monastic contemplation that came to Lister and Archibald and Halsted. Many never thought of carrying out original work of their own until after graduation.

But whatever the background and whatever the local conditions, something of a different order is required of all of us. Each surgeon, and each physician, must learn to know the meaning of compassion. If he is worthy of the Hippocratic tradition he must be alert to the hopes and the fears of his patients – he must qualify as their confidant, counsellor and judge. This is a medical qualification that is sometimes overlooked.

Because of our great responsibility for the lives of other men, the scientific attitude must be introduced into surgery only with caution. It must be controlled by much experience. We begin to practise our profession with the guidance of traditional teaching and with the help of our current reading. But once entered into practice, we must face our failures.

Here is where surgeons meet their most searching test. Some will take these failures as a challenge. And those who are scientists at heart will then set out to find what is wrong for themselves, realizing that the final authority does not lie in the precepts of former teachers, nor in textbooks. Such a surgeon will turn to his own observation of man in health and disease, and discover that the final authority lies in the patient before him.

Thus, it may be that a day of second graduation will come to him – when he has studied his unsolved problem during life and in death, on the operating table and afterward, with patience and with determination. Then he may pass through the gates of science into a new fellowship. He will find himself a member of the most honoured company of explorers – and he will feel a new excitement like a cool wind coming down to him from the mountains of the unknown land.

Some will be worthy to wear the mantle of John Stewart and some perhaps the mantle of Lister.

Aegean Cradle of Medicine

For two years I have been engaged in a voyage of exploration into the conditions that preceded, and ushered in, the dawn of Medicine. We have, ready to hand in the Hippocratic writings, a clear conception of scientific medicine freed from superstition and prejudice, and with it the ethics that alone can make Medicine respectable. How could all this have come from the mind of a single man, a practically unknown man? Surely he did not discover Medicine rising in all her beauty from the blue waters of the Aegean like Aphrodite!

About two thousand years before Christ there was an invasion of the Greek peninsula and the northern islands of the Aegean Sea by Indo-Europeans from the region of the Danube. They were called Achaeans, a rough strong people using bronze tools and weapons. They worshipped Mother Earth and Father Sky and the Sun, later to be called Hera and Zeus and Apollo. Fortunately, the first conquering wave of invaders did not go too far. They settled down and learned from the civilization to the south of them.

The second wave of invasion from the north came about 1200 B.C., when the Dorians swept south and settled in the Peloponnesus. They colonized the southern coast of Asia Minor and the southern islands of the Aegean. Crete fell to them, and the Cretan civilization, from which the Achaean had learned so much, disappeared.

In the ninth century Homer wrote the Iliad, collecting the stories of the siege of Troy, an event which had occurred about

FROM THE S. WEIR MITCHELL ORATION, PHILADELPHIA; FEBRUARY 1956.

three hundred years earlier. Twice he referred to the blameless physician of Thrace whose name was Asclepius. Asclepius is better known to us by the Latin name, Aesculapius, but I shall use that form only when speaking of him in his later role as the god of medicine.

The Greeks brought with them, to the siege of Troy, two physicians. Homer called them "cunning leeches." They were the sons of Asclepius. "A leech," he wrote, "is of the worth of many other men, for the cutting out of arrows and the spreading of soothing simples."

Between the twelfth century B.C. when Troy fell and the fifth century when Hippocrates was born, there were two lines of evolution. On the one hand the descendants of Asclepius became the true physicians. They called themselves Asclepiads (Hippocrates was one of them) and they handed down their knowledge and skill from father to son. On the other hand the Grecian story-tellers gradually altered the figure of Asclepius, the blameless physician of Thessaly, and made him the god of medicine, creating a splendid myth.

Sometime after the ninth century Aesculapius was established as the god of healing, and it has been claimed that between eighty and a hundred shrines and temples were built in different cities in his honour. He was provided with antecedents and descendants appropriate to his rank. He was made the son of the nymph Coronis by Apollo, the beautiful sun god, and his birth-place was moved from Tricca to Epidaurus. They even raised his newly created daughters, Hygeia and Panacea, to the rank of goddesses and gave him a new son called Iaso. Aesculapius was said to have been educated by the centaur Chiron who taught him, along with Achilles, how to treat the sick.

Furthermore, his elevation to the rank of god was explained, you remember, as follows: He became so successful, as a man in the practice of medicine, that Pluto, god of the underworld, complained to Zeus of a serious shortage of shades in Hades, whereupon the Father of the Gods destroyed Aesculapius with a thunderbolt. But this was no sooner accomplished than Zeus relented and elevated him to the great Olympian company of the immortals.

The temples of Aesculapius were called Asclepions and in

them patients were treated for all manner of disease. It was the custom in these Asclepions that sufferers would sleep in a covered colonnade called an abaton. After nightfall the priest of Aesculapius would walk among the sleepers and waken them one by one to talk with each about his complaints. The priest was followed on his rounds by large harmless earth-snakes that must have increased his power of suggestion enormously. These snakes were plentiful at Epidaurus, where the most famous and one of the first of his shrines was built, and the serpent served to identify him in the minds of the people with the older Dorian earth-god who had been followed by mystic snakes.

But the priest had more than the power of faith-healing at his command, for the patient could be referred to operating surgeons in the god's clinic on the following day or to the trained temple gymnasts who were skilled in the most elaborate uses of exercise, massage, baths. The most celebrated of the Asclepions were the following three: the one at Tricca, near the real birth-place of Asclepius, the one at Epidaurus where his miraculous birth was supposed to have occurred, and the shrine on the Island of Cos where Hippocrates was born.

And there, to Epidaurus, I travelled with my wife. We did not go to it by water, as the ancient Greeks would probably have done. We made our modern pilgrimage in a tiny Citröen driven by our friend Doros Oeconomos, the Athenian neuro-surgeon. We crossed the Corinthian isthmus to the Peloponnesus, passing through Corinth, once the wealthy and sinful city whose women welcomed all comers with such luxurious hospitality. We stopped, in retrospective wonder, at the ruins of Mycenae where Agamemnon had summoned the Achaeans to a council of war before sailing away to the siege of Troy. That was when Asclepius was still a practising physician, long before his divine rebirth.

The ruins of Epidaurus are above the sea in the hills of Argolis. We wandered through the ruins, rebuilding in fancy the beautiful temple of white marble and watching, in our imagination, the stream of men and women, rich and poor, passing through its pillars to look at the statue of Aesculapius as he sat facing the morning sun, with bearded face and kindly expression, the staff in his hand and the snake coiling up the staff.

As the people walked out of the temple again, they must have heard the humming voices of the multitude and the water splashing from the mouth of a towering statue that stood before the entrance – splashing into a basin from which many drank and stood up again, feeling strong and saying that even this would make them well.

To the left was the colonnaded abaton where the sick would sleep the night, and through the columns they could see the distant valley. Beside the temple was the surgical pavilion where wounds were dressed and small operations carried out on stone tables by the temple surgeons. The surgeons used the delicately made instruments which have been picked up there and are preserved now for inspection: curettes, scalpels, self-retaining retractors, thumb forceps.

On the other side of the temple they might look down on the sports stadium and then, turning back, might walk through the enormous gymnasium, watching the expert gymnasts at work. From there they would pass the therapeutic baths and join the throng in the great open square or enter one of the hotels of the well-to-do. From the square it was only a few minutes' stroll up the hillside to the outdoor theatre where fourteen thousand people could watch the drama, and listen to music and oratory.

We left the ruins and climbed the slope to this outdoor theatre, which is remarkably preserved. It is shaped like half a bowl set into the side of the hill. The aisles, that lead outward and upward, radiate in perfect symmetry from the round stage. We climbed to the topmost bank of seats while our guide remained standing on the stage. He spoke in a low voice to demonstrate the remarkable acoustics.

How often did those who sat here listen to the voice of young Hippolytus* as he lay mortally wounded on the stage below:

Weep for me, weep for me,
Scarred, broken, trampled under foot.

. . .

---

* Euripides – *Hippolytus*, in *Alcestis and Other Plays*, translated by P. Vellacott, Penguin Books, 1953.

In vain I strove with patience
To love and serve my neighbour:
Now pain sets painful foot upon my body.
Let go, hold me no longer,
But let Death come to heal me;
And, if you pity me, help me to die quickly!

.   .   .

I am in love with the rending spear: Come cruel edge,
Cleave my heart and lull my life asleep!

What a plea for euthanasia! And then the chorus in swaying robes of grey and purple, chanting:

Oh, for that quiet garden by the Western Sea
Where the daughters of the Evening sing
Under the golden apple-tree ...

The Greeks loved beauty, beauty of nature, beauty of the mind, beauty of the body. Young men rejoiced to match their naked strength against their equals and old men took pride in the exercise of their intellects. Competition was certainly a most important element in Greek life, competition of mind as well as body. Every city, large or small, had its theatre where men might weep at tragedy and roar aloud with raucous laughter at the coarsest comedy.

Take, for example, a passage from the rowdy play of Aristophanes, called *Plutus*. Curiously enough, this gives the best description that has come down to us of the "temple sleep" which was employed for psychotherapy. Cario, a slave, describes his night in the abaton to the wife of his master. He refers to the statues of the god Aesculapius and his son Iaso and his daughter Hygeia. Then he tells of the night as follows:

Soon the Temple servitor
Put out the lights, and bade us fall asleep,
Nor stir, nor speak, whatever noise we heard.
So down we lay in orderly repose.
And I could catch no slumber, not one wink,
Struck by a nice tureen of broth which stood

A little distance from an old wife's head,
Whereto I marvellously longed to creep.
Then, glancing upwards, I beheld the priest
Whipping the cheese-cakes and the figs from off
The holy table; thence he coasted round
To every altar, spying from what was left.
And everything he found he consecrated
Into a sort of sack; so I, concluding
This was the right and proper thing to do,
Arose at once to tackle that tureen.

WIFE: *Unhappy man! Did you not fear the god?*

CARIO: *Indeed I did, lest he should cut in first,*
Garlands and all, and capture my tureen.
For so the priest forwarned me he might do.
Then the old lady when my steps she heard
Reached out a stealthy hand; I gave a hiss,
And mouthed it gently like a sacred snake.
Back flies her hand; she draws her coverlets
More tightly round her, and, beneath them, lies
In deadly terror like a frightened cat.
Then of the broth I gobbled down a lot
Till I could eat no more, and then I stopped.

WIFE: *Did not the god approach you?*

CARIO: *Not till later.*
And then I did a thing will make you laugh.
For as he neared me, by some dire mishap
My wind exploded like a thunder-clap.

WIFE: *I guess the god was awfully disgusted.*

CARIO: *No, but Iaso blushed a rosy red*
And Panacea turned away her head
Holding her nose: my wind's not frankincense.

It was the way of the Greeks, this mocking of things they held most dear. The great Socrates probably laughed at this comedy. And yet, on his last day, after he had drunk the deadly hemlock and was waiting for death to come upon him, he roused for a moment and said to his friend: "Crito, we ought to offer a cock to Asclepius. See to it, and don't forget."

A final sacrifice, a debt to be paid to Aesculapius! These were the last words of that philosopher who approached most closely by the way of reason to the Christian concept of God; the man Plato called, "the bravest and also the wisest and most upright."

From those topmost seats in the theatre at Epidaurus we could look down on the stage, the temple ruins beyond, the stadium and the rolling green slopes of the valley far below. As we climbed down the stone steps again the wind was cool and bracing. It brought with it the spicy scent of the pine forest, where the earth-snakes still abound though men seem to have forgotten about the healing power of their slippery bodies. The good water no longer gushes from a god's mouth, but it bubbles up still from the ground.

We drank it and ate fresh figs, talking with the wife of the guide who stood, as she talked, whirling her distaff while the snow-white wool grew into twisted thread. Somehow we too felt refreshed and strong like the pilgrims of long ago.

The patients who came to the shrine in old times were urged to leave behind them testimonials to the healing power of Aesculapius, and many did so. A man who wrote that he had been cured of "paralysis and *oedema*" donated a marble carving of himself which may still be seen. In the carving, he lies on the ground with head and back arched and arms and legs extended in powerful contraction. The sculpture is so good that no other diagnosis than hysteria could be made.

The cult of Aesculapius was based on superstition and on the belief that devils and gods struggle for bad and good in our bodies and in our minds. Nevertheless, it has since provided the medical profession with a sort of mythology of our own. The rod and the coiled earth-snake of the Greek god is now our cherished emblem.

Coming away from Epidaurus, we stopped to see a Greek Orthodox church on a hill in the town of Nauplion. Here, pinned below one of the ikons, were many little testimonials of healing written on metal and on paper. The grateful messages of these testimonials were quite similar to those hung upon the walls of the Asclepion long, long ago.

Faith in our God still cures the broken heart and the troubled spirit. There can be no doubt that man will always have need of such healing, however much the ways of worship may change on the one hand and however far scientific medicine may progress on the other.

But all this had little to do with medicine itself and nothing to do with medical science. In the fifth century before Christ it is apparent that there were two medical schools, one at Cos, an island in the Aegean Sea, and the other at Cnidus, which was about fifteen miles away on the coast of Caria, now called Asia Minor or Anatolia.

The teachers in each school, if schools they may be called, belonged to the family of Asclepiads, which claimed direct descent from Asclepius; their students were sons, or apprentices who paid stated fees to be admitted to the family and to be taught the theory and the practice of medicine. They are not to be confused with the priests of Aesculapius. The god was mentioned only once in the Hippocratic writings and that was in the Hippocratic oath.

The Asclepion was built on the island of Cos about 350 B.C. – 110 years after the birth of Hippocrates – probably replacing an altar to Aesculapius which had stood in the famous grove of Apollo.

All of this renders more than absurd the statements of the historian Pliny who, writing in the first century A.D., stated that Hippocrates had been able to learn and to institute "that medicine which is called 'bedside medicine' " from reading the testimonials which patients had inscribed in gratitude upon the walls of the Asclepion of Cos, and furthermore, that he had burned the temple down so that others might not know the source of this great knowledge!

The first reference to the family of Asclepiads appears in the writings of Theopompus, who stated that they came from Syrnus, a town in Caria. The coast of Caria (Asia Minor), together with the adjacent islands, was divided into three general districts: Aeolian to the north, Ionic in the mid-portion, and Doric to the south.

The six great Dorian seaport cities of the South Aegean (Cos, Cnidus, Halicarnassos, and the three cities on the island of

Rhodes – Lindos, Ialysos, and Camiros) formed a Doric Hexapolis largely for the purposes of sports competitions in honour of Apollo. These games were held at Cnidus,* and occasionally an outstanding athlete from one of the cities was able to bring honour to his city by winning at the Olympic Games. This is of considerable importance, for the records of the sports of these cities are much better preserved than the records of governments or of the two centres of medical teaching. The sports records throw a good deal of light on the way of life.

Although the settlements were Doric, the Hippocratic writings were in Ionic Greek like the poetry of Homer and the books of the first historian, Herodotus. Herodotus was born in Halicarnassos and was contemporary with Hippocrates. The first great philosophers were Ionic. Thales was a Milesian and Pythagoras came from the island of Samos north of Cos.

Next to nothing is known of the actual life of Hippocrates, although the impact of his thinking on posterity was so great. Galen, who was born in Pergamus (Caria) in 130 A.D., was a most ardent admirer of Hippocrates and made much propaganda of his teachings. But some of the sources to which Galen had access have disappeared.

A contemporary of Galen's, Soranus by name, a physician of Ephesus, whom Galen apparently disliked, wrote a short biography of Hippocrates drawn from such records as he could find five hundred years after his death. The account states that Hippocrates was born in Cos, a descendant of Hercules and of Asclepius, the twentieth generation from the one and the nineteenth from the other.

According to the Archives of Cos, the biographer continues, he was born on the 18th day of the month of Agrianus, a day long set apart by the Coans for his honour. "He left his own country for burning the library in Cnidus, if we may believe a malicious writer, Andreas, in his book of the Origin of Physick."

Obviously, this accusation is as preposterous as the tale that Pliny had told a century earlier, since it would hardly be consistent with the high character of the man as judged by other

---

* This bit of history, we later discovered, was erroneous to this extent – the games were held a few miles away, at Triopion.

evidence, especially the Hippocratic writings. Strange gossip to have survived five hundred years!

However, the story is important for it is the only historical suggestion that there were libraries in those days and that a medical one existed in Cnidus. It might well have been the private library of the leader of the Cnidean Asclepiads. But it seems likely that there was a similar library in Cos, and that when the writings of Hippocrates were collected in Alexandria by order of Ptolemy II a century later, the collection was made up of scrolls from such libraries.

The biographer continues with the description of the great successes of Hippocrates as a physician, and how he refused the invitation of various kings to come to other countries. Finally, when Artaxerxes urged him to come to Persia, "offering him, at the same time, great rewards; he, from a regard to decency, a contempt of riches and a love of his country, refused him . . ."

He died in Thessaly, in the city of Larissa, having "taught his art, with great candour and liberality, to those who were studious of it."

Then the biographer adds the charming remark that near his monument "a flight of bees made their honey for a long time," and it is reported that children who were anointed with the honey by their nurses, at the side of his grave, were cured of "aphtha's" or little ulcers in the mouth.

Cos is a wind-swept island, mountainous for the most part, but with pleasant foothills and valleys. It is about thirty miles in length and three or four miles in width at the widest. On the west end there is now a village called Cephalos, high on the hill above the beautiful bay of Camara. This was the site of the most ancient capital, which was called Astypalia. It was apparently from here that ships were sent to join the other Greeks when they besieged Troy under the leadership of Agamemnon.

Sometime before the fourth century B.C., the chief seaport of the island was built on the eastern end of the island at Cos Meropis on the site of the present city of Cos. Hippocrates probably left Cos soon after the outbreak of the Peloponnesian War in 431 B.C. Certain earlier scholars believed that this transfer of the capital took place after that time (Sudhoff, 1930), but later evidence indicates that the time was much earlier.

Laurenzie* studied the ruins of the present city after the earthquake of 1933 and found what he considers to be a large pre-
Hellenistic city there.

At the time of that earthquake, a tablet of Pentelic, or
Athenian, marble was shaken out of one of the houses in the
present city. The tablet, which had obviously been sent from
Athens to be set up in the city's market-place, bore an inscription demanding that the city should pay, as a member of the
Delian League, a tribute to Athens of three talents. This bore
the date when Hippocrates would have been a young man.

It is in the present city also, in a carefully guarded enclosure
near the shore that looks to the east toward Halicarnassos, that
the famous plane tree of Hippocrates stands. The Islanders
maintain, and have done so for many centuries, that it was
beneath this tree that Hippocrates taught his disciples. It is
dwarfed as to height but has an enormous hollow trunk, forty-
five feet in circumference. Sturdy new trunks are growing up
from its roots.

During the four hundred years of Turkish occupation, it
was guarded by them carefully and the branches supported by
stone pillars. They built a mosque before it so that the tree
now stands in front of the mosque built by the Turks and
behind the Governor's Palace, built by the Italians during
their brief occupation between the two world wars. All the
world reveres Hippocrates, especially those whom the Greeks
once called Barbarians.

I must conclude that the evidence is strongly in favour of the
truth of the legendary tradition. Hippocrates the Second, whom
we may call Hippocrates the Great, the Father of Medicine,
lived and taught here at the eastern end of the island; and perhaps his father Heracleides and his grandfather Hippocrates
the First before him.

Many of the inscriptions found on the island of Cos by Paton
and Hicks (1891) refer to Hippocrates and to members of his
family. His mother, Praxithea, and his grandmother, Phae-
narete, seem to have come from the pleasant farming town on
the south shore, half way between the ancient Astypalia and the

* Personal communication.

more recent Cos Meropis. There are references, likewise, to his brother Soranus, who was also an Asclepiad.

Contemporary with Hippocrates was the great leader of the Cnidian Asclepiads, Euryphon, a physician with a special interest in the diseases of women. The Cnidian School was probably older than that of Cos. Most scholars agree that some of his writings are included with those of Hippocrates in the Corpus Hippocraticum. Euryphon was probably the author of a book called the Cnidian Sentences that was still in existence at the time of Galen, but disappeared some time after that.

Ctesias was another famous physician of Cnidus. He became court physician to the Persian king Artaxerxes and spent much of his life there. He wrote a history of Assyria and Persia in twenty-three volumes; a work with which Xenophon was familiar. The history unfortunately was lost and we know little of Ctesias the physician.

The writings of these physicians were probably collected in the following century after the centre of Greek culture had moved to Egypt in the wake of the conquests of Alexander the Great. There, at the new court in Alexandria, Herophilos, a physician from Cos, wrote commentaries on the doctrines of Hippocrates and discussed his terminology. There also Erasistratos of Cnidus upheld the teachings of the rival school. There, no doubt, schools from various parts of the world copied and translated the writings of the Aegean Asclepiads and carried their copies away to various cities of Europe and Asia before the destruction of the Alexandrian Library.

It was not until the tenth century A.D. that an effort was made to collect, re-translate and edit the works then attributed to Hippocrates. In 1861, Littré finally completed a splendid translation of the Corpus Hippocraticum into French, a task to which he had given twenty-three years of his life. And in the first decade of the twentieth century, there appeared a scholarly English translation by the philologist, W. H. S. Jones, whose discussions and introductions added much to the text.*

---

* Professor Henry Sigerist (1934) has urged that every English-speaking physician should own this work which appears in four small volumes in the Loeb Classical Library Series, entitled *Hippocrates*.

There are in the Corpus Hippocraticum discussions that reflect a certain rivalry and difference of opinion between Cos and Cnidus. It contains textbooks for physicians, textbooks for laymen, pieces of research, lectures for medical students, essays by philosophers on the fringe of medicine, and notebooks or scrap-books. Many are unfinished and none is signed. There are no originals; all have been copied and recopied through the ages.

But in spite of all that, it is clear that certain books were written by a great man, a man who stood by the bedside of many a patient looking at the face of disease until he learned to predict the outcome. He passed over those things that he could not know and suppressed the irrelevant. He swept away religious superstition and the unprovable assumptions of philosophy, to record what he could see and hear and feel. He based his reasoning on observed fact and learned to assist the body in its vital struggle against disease. He reduced fractures and he carried out operations. He established a wise regimen, taking thought for the mind as well as the body, and making a careful record of his failures, for the instruction of others.

The man who wrote the best tracts, and left the most perfect clinical case records of disease that were to appear for two thousand years, was a genius. He saw more clearly than other men in his time. No one can bring the final proof that the name of this genius was Hippocrates, nor can it be disproven.

Plato quoted Socrates as saying that "Hippocrates of Cos, of the house of the Asclepiads" was a physician as distinguished in medicine as Phidias, greatest of Greek sculptors, in his art. Again, Plato reported a discussion which Socrates carried out with his pupil Phaedo regarding the opinion of Hippocrates, of the Asclepiad family, on a philosophical question – the relation of the soul to the body (or the universe). They did not inquire as to what other physicians might think of the matter. And Aristotle used him as a symbol of greatness a generation later: "Hippocrates," he wrote, "would be called greater, not as a man but as a physician, than a man who is superior to him in stature."

So many writings must have been lost. Who can say? They may have been superior to those that have come down to us.

But those we have are random samples of the medical thought in Cos and Cnidus. If the great leader did not write the best of them; if, like his contemporary, Socrates, he only taught by word of mouth, he was no less great. On the whole, it seems fair to assume that the best works in the Corpus are the direct or indirect expression of the thinking of Hippocrates the Second.

Finally, listen to the voice of Hippocrates. Sometimes I shall quote directly, sometimes paraphrase with the help of Singer (1921), Elisha Bartlett (1852) or Osler (1921).

"Do not believe that the gods cause illness and madness and do not hope to bring healing and help to the sufferer by means of magic or spells or false sorceries. Know rather that we must turn to nature itself, to the observation of the body in health and disease to learn the truth.

"Men ought to know that from the brain and the brain only, arise our pleasures, joys, laughter and jests, as well as our sorrow, pains, griefs and tears. Through it, in particular, we think, see, hear and distinguish the ugly from the beautiful, the bad from the good, the pleasant from the unpleasant. . . ."

"It is the same thing which makes us mad or delirious, inspires us with dread or fear, whether by night or by day, brings sleeplessness, inopportune mistakes, aimless anxieties, absent-mindedness, and acts that are contrary to habit. These things that we suffer all come from the brain when it is not healthy. . . ."

"He who would become a good physician must have a natural disposition; instruction; favourable position for study; early tuition; love of labour; leisure."

When in doubt every physician should ask for medical consultation. "At all times he should make no effort to dazzle the patient; give no lectures for the purpose of increasing his reputation, and resist the temptation to trick out teaching with quotations from the poets; make no pretence to infallibility; have regard to personal cleanliness, use elegance without luxury and perfumes with restraint."

"Life is short, art is long, opportunity is fugitive, experience is deceptive, judgment difficult."

Where Shall Wisdom Be Found?

ELEVEN

Surely there is a vein for the silver,
and a place for gold where they fine it.

But where shall wisdom be found?
and where is the place of understanding? (JOB 28)

The most outstanding figure among the teachers of medicine in ancient Greece was Hippocrates. He was born in 460 B.C., the year that Pericles came to power in Athens. Literature, art, mathematics, philosophy flowered during a single century. In this fruitful age of intellectual germination, modern medicine and science itself were born. During the lifetime of Hippocrates, Nehemiah led a remnant of the Hebrew race back from captivity to Jerusalem, to build its walls again with Persia's help. It was then that the writing of the Old Testament was finished. It closed with self-reproach and talk of final judgment. There were wistful recollections of the law and a promise of the coming of Elijah and of the "great and dreadful day of the Lord." But the grandeur of creative religious thought to be found in Job and Psalms and Proverbs had disappeared.

References to physicians are very rare in either Testament, old or new, and those references often suggest a considerable amount of contempt. No doubt it was deserved. It is true that Luke was called the "beloved physician," but there is no evidence that his skill as a physician was held in respect. We are reminded more than once that those who were cured by faith

HOSPITAL-SUNDAY ADDRESS, CHRIST CHURCH CATHEDRAL, MONTREAL; MAY 25, 1958.

had previously spent all their "living upon physicians" to no avail.

Of Asa, King of Judah, it is written that he "was diseased in his feet, until his disease was exceeding great; yet in his disease he sought not to the Lord, but to physicians.

"And Asa . . . died in the one and fortieth year of his reign."*

This competition, in the Hebrew mind, between God and the physician, could have had only one outcome! There were no healers worthy of the name of physician in Israel. The precept that sin was the cause of disease, and that health was the reward of good behaviour, made sickly soil for medical growth.

If there were a bible of modern medicine, the first book would be called the Hippocratic Writings and the date would be set at the fifth to fourth centuries before Christ. Hippocrates prepared the way for the birth of scientific medicine in Greece by declaring that diseases came from natural causes, not from gods or devils. Physician is a Greek word which means one who studies nature, a naturalist, and with the new word came a new conception. But, added Hippocrates, in one sense all that happens in Nature might be considered divine. Physicians must study Nature and examine man in health and in disease—must observe, record, compare. Nature herself, he said, brings healing. The physician can give great help by planning a wise regime, by drugs and by surgery. But first he must understand and predict the reaction of the body when disease or injury comes to it. It may be said that modern medicine, and modern science too, were born when Hippocrates defined the scientific method. To know is science. To think one knows, without study, is ignorance.

But, surprising though it may seem, along with science came human kindness and a lofty conception of honour. This is not really surprising since man was the subject of study, not something inanimate. In those days, disciples who could pay the fee for medical tuition sailed from all parts of Greece across the Aegean Sea to the Island of Cos. They came to study medicine under Hippocrates, if we may believe the words of Socrates in

---

* Second Chronicles 16:12,13.

Plato's *Protagoras*. And one may assume that when a disciple was accepted he swore the Hippocratic Oath which has been found with the other writings. I may summarize this vow as follows:

"I swear . . . that I will carry out, according to my ability and judgment, this oath and this indenture.

"To hold my teacher in this art equal to my own parents . . . to consider his family as my brothers, and to teach them this art, if they want to learn it . . .

"I will use treatment to help the sick according to my ability and judgment, but never with a view to injury and wrongdoing. Neither will I administer a poison when asked to do so . . . Similarly I will not give a woman a pessary to cause abortion. But I will keep pure and holy both my life and art.

"Into whatsoever houses I enter, I will enter to help the sick, and I will abstain from all intentional wrongdoing with man or woman, bond or free.

"And whatsoever I hear or see in the course of my profession, as well as outside my profession, if it be what should not be published abroad, I will never divulge, holding such things to be holy secrets.

"Now if I carry out this oath, and break it not, may I gain forever reputation among all men for my life, and for my art . . ."

How astonishing to hear these words spoken in the fifth century at a time when the Jewish spiritual light had flickered and seemed to have gone out. This was a code of honour to those who practised the art of medicine. But it was more than a code. It established something that approaches a religion.

"I will keep pure and holy both my life and my art."

Thus Hippocrates set Medicine apart from other arts and other skills. He set up for it an ethical beacon. Practitioners were destined to look up to the beacon for centuries, however meagre their knowledge of the art might be. They still do, for it shines as clear to us today as it did for them on the far-away island of Cos, so long ago.

But the Oath does not stand alone among the Hippocratic writings. For example, in a later lecture entitled "Precepts" the following is found:

"Sometimes give your services for nothing . . . and if there be an opportunity of serving one who is a stranger in financial straits, give full assistance to all such. For where there is love of man, there is also love of the art."

Sir William Osler, once of Montreal and always our Canadian medical hero, said that what Socrates achieved in philosophy, Hippocrates did for medicine. In a sense that is true. I like to think that Hippocrates, who was eight years younger, may have listened to Socrates, as a pupil in Athens for a time. It is quite clear that both men looked beyond Zeus and Apollo and Athena and the other Olympian gods. Beyond Mount Olympus they perceived the presence of God, the God of the universe. Both men sought the truth, Hippocrates in nature and in the body of man, Socrates in the spirit of man.

The Greek people, during the classical period, were something new and strange upon the face of the earth. You have only to compare them with the so-called Barbarian peoples about them. They were keener and swifter in mind and body. They had an instinct for temperance and beauty. They admired excellence in every field of endeavour, physical and intellectual. In each area they devised new techniques and persisted until a new art emerged. So it was that medicine was born.

"Doubtless there is, in every art," wrote Gilbert Murray, late Regius Professor of Greek at Oxford, "an element of mere knowledge or science, and that element is progressive. But there is another element, too, which does not depend on knowledge and which does not progress but has a kind of stationary and eternal value, like the beauty of the dawn, or the love of a mother for her child, or the joy of a young animal in being alive, or the courage of a martyr facing torment. We cannot for all our progress get beyond these things: there they stand like light upon the mountains."*

The art of medicine is made up of the two elements described by Professor Murray. The first is science. How amazingly it has grown, and how it will continue to grow! Medical science has found the cure for a hundred diseases, brought relief of pain,

---

* Gilbert Murray, "The Value of Greece to the Modern World", Chapter I in *The Legacy of Greece*, ed. R. W. Livingstone. Oxford, 1921.

health, long life to the human race. But the second element is based on honour and on the love of man.. That has not changed in 2,400 years. The oath of Hippocrates is not outdated. It has an eternal value that is akin to religion.

Years ago, when scholarship and science were roused from the lethargy of the Middle Ages and there was an awakening, a renaissance, of Greek learning, the organized Church was fearful of science. Galileo was summoned from Pisa to Rome and told that he must not prove that the world moved about the sun. He must deny it, since it contradicted church interpretation of bible history. So Galileo knelt. He denied what he knew to be true.

That day of misunderstanding is long past. And yet, there is a lingering suspicion in the minds of some that those scientists who worked on evolution and on astronomy and such things were, after all, guilty creatures who disturbed the peace of the "godly" and made them begin to think unnecessarily.

There seems to be a tradition, too, that no good scientist can be a good Christian. This is sheer nonsense! Science casts no light on the nature of mind and spirit; not yet. Perhaps it never will. The actual relationship between these things and the brain is still quite unknown. Materialism is not scientific. Materialism is a matter of faith. It is a kind of religion to which many cling in ignorance, believing that the machine has already explained the spirit. It will be a very long time before science throws definite light on the true nature of the mind. What that light will be, no one can know. But for no sincere person, no honest body of religious thought, no worthy creed, need there be fear of the truth.

The scientist who believes in God, in the after-life, in the message of Christ, arrives at his belief just as the non-scientist does. It is an act of reasonable faith. If he is a good scientist, he is aware that science cannot help him one way or the other. He adopts the belief that seems to him reasonable. He cannot wait for proofs. He must live his life and plan to die like other men.

Many thinking men, scientists among them, reserve the right to interpret history for themselves, wherever the record may be found. They may even differ with the clergy, from time to time, in regard to history. Basic beliefs are another matter. Basic beliefs have an "eternal value". "There they stand like light upon the mountains."

I have talked of religion and of medicine. I hope I have shown the growing kinship between these two. But what about the broad field of science? A similar relationship must hold there. Science is no more than understanding, the understanding of the truth in nature. Unfortunately, science has made it possible for governments, duly elected by the people, to build the atom bomb. We fear what this may do. But physicists cannot unlearn the secrets of the atom. Truth cannot be put back into the womb of Nature. Truth must be faced. Scientists will inevitably continue to advance to new truth, greater understanding.

The problem before us today is to match understanding with wisdom. The atom bomb threatens an unworthy generation. This threat is not for today alone but for always. The eventual cure for our unworthiness, the only safeguard against extinction, is friendship and universal brotherly love. Mahatma Gandhi reached the millions of India for a time, teaching this ideal. Medicine has no enemies and physicians are friends around the world, for they are united in common service to man. But something more is needed.

What are we waiting for? Is it a new religion to draw the peoples of the world together in brotherly understanding, accepting science and the world as it is, forgetting the frontiers of creed and sect?

"But where shall wisdom be found?

"Destruction and death say, We have heard the fame thereof with our ears.

"Behold, the fear of the Lord, that is wisdom; and to depart from evil is understanding."

The Neurophysiology of Speech and Some Educational Consequences

[TWELVE]

The great difference between man and the other mammals is that man can learn to speak and to understand the meaning of speech. It is by means of the spoken and the written word that the ignorance of childhood is changed into the understanding thought of educated men and women.

Bees have a language, as Karl von Frisch has described so entertainingly. Dogs, monkeys, birds communicate with their own kind. But they use a language which is largely inherited, inborn.

Man has a spoken language which must be taught to each growing child. His ability to learn to speak depends upon the post-natal organization of speech mechanisms within his brain. When a baby comes into the world the speech areas of the cerebral cortex are like a clean slate, ready to be written upon. Other forms of movement and sensation, on the other hand, depend on inborn mechanisms which resemble those of other mammals.

When the gross structure of the human brain is compared with that of animals, no new speech organ is evident. The brain of the dog resembles ours in general organization, and that of the chimpanzee still more so. All the lobes which form its major subdivisions are present. The pathways of muscular control are like ours. They have large areas of cerebral cortex devoted to seeing and hearing and feeling, and even larger areas for smelling.

AN ADDRESS TO THE AMERICAN ACADEMY OF ARTS AND SCIENCES, BOSTON; FEBRUARY 1953.

Animals learn from experience, as we do, and they remember what they have learned. More than that, they seem to have unique racial memories which guide them in their behaviour, especially at crucial times in their lives. This memory, which we call instinctive, is strangely lacking in us.

If we did not teach, and if we could not learn, we would be more helpless than all other mammals. In the observations which follow it is my purpose to question the accepted methods of teaching foreign language. I venture to do this, not because I claim any specialized knowledge of pedagogy, but from the point of view of familiarity with the cerebral speech mechanisms and their derangements.

Speaking, and the understanding of speech, also reading and writing depend upon the employment of certain specialized areas of the cerebrum. There is an optimum age when these special areas are plastic and receptive, and my purpose in this rambling, pseudo-scientific discussion is merely to remind educators of this fact.

In the history of our race, we know little of the beginnings of speech. It has been said that it was when man learned to cultivate grain in the valleys of the Nile and the Euphrates that the birth of civilization was made possible. But there was a more important prerequisite to that civilization – the learning of a language. The writing of that language came later, and its evolution can be traced in the tablets of Mesopotamia.

I remember a day when I stepped out of the blazing sun of a street in Baghdad into the Iraq Museum. There, in the museum's half light, I saw rows of clay tablets, each of them shaped like a piece of soap. On them could be seen the stages in the story of writing from picture-drawing and counting to alphabet.

Seton Lloyd, then Curator of the Museum, picked up a tablet and held it in the palm of his hand just as some Sumerian scribe must have held it when it was soft clay more than five thousand years ago. He pointed out the pictograph of a bag of barley and the single mark of the stylus which stood for the number ten (the number of a man's fingers) and the different marks which were used to represent ones. Here was a record of sale at a time when men had learned to cultivate grain in that fertile plain, a time when speech was probably quite well-developed and when man was about to turn from pictograph to writing, an evolution which seems to have been relatively rapid.

Today we have learned to understand something of the cerebral mechanisms which enabled man to begin to speak, and later to write and read. I shall describe these in simple outline.

The two cerebral hemispheres of man are homologous. They are mirror images of each other. The cerebral cortex, the carpet of nerve cells that covers each hemisphere, is identical in structure when the two sides are compared.

Animals employ each hemisphere for movement and sensation on the opposite side of the body, as we do. Nerve impulses which utilize these twin hemispheres come from central or centrencephalic grey matter in the brain-stem that joins the two. But the function of each is like that of the other.

When a child begins to speak, there develops a functional specialization in one cerebral hemisphere, normally the left hemisphere where the right hand is also represented. There are separate areas of the cortex on this, the dominant, side which come to be devoted to the formulation and the understanding of speech. Thus a mechanism is established for the ideational purposes of speech.* It is somewhat like the movement of a watch in the following respect. Interference with one of its parts causes it to stop or to slow down, although each part may well play a very different role in the perfect functioning of this mechanism.

But there is more to speaking than the ideational process involved. There is articulation produced by control of mouth, lips and tongue, and there is vocalization produced by control of the larynx and the muscles of respiration, including the diaphragm. There are four areas of the human cortex from which vocalization can be produced by electrical stimulation, two in the right hemisphere and two in the left. It seems likely that each of these cortical areas is able to activate, by its connections, a common mechanism in the brain-stem, for when a stimulating electrode is placed on any of the four areas, the

---

* On page 143 (Fig. 2) the reader will find a sketch on which is shown the principal area devoted to the ideational purposes of speech.

patient is caused to make a similar involuntary cry, a long-drawn-out vowel sound.

On the other hand, stimulation of the motor areas of the cortex of the chimpanzee, the dog, or the cat does not produce vocalization, although these animals are able to vocalize, each in its own way, from the day of birth. One may surmise, then, that in the case of man there is establishment of four additional representations of vocalization in the cerebral cortex, and that each of these four areas preserves an activating connection with the vocalization centre in the brain-stem. One may assume also that the appearance of this representation in the cortex is closely related to man's ability to speak.

The new-born kitten or the new-born puppy raises its voice to announce the pangs of hunger, that seem to usher it into the world, just as effectively as the new-born baby does. But, at a later period when the cerebral cortex begins to function, only the child is ready to learn to speak. Both child and animal have the capacity to control the mouth and to vocalize but the child, beginning at about the end of the first year of life, uses a small part of the cortex of one hemisphere for the purpose of speech understanding and speech formulation. This area holds the recordings which make reading possible, and writing as well. All these things which we may refer to as the ideational processes of speech depend upon the integrity of a part of one hemisphere, not both. This, as already pointed out, is usually the left hemisphere. By it the right hand, the dominant hand, is also controlled.

Thus, it is apparent that, at birth, mechanisms for movement and sensation are pre-formed. The infant vocalizes and uses its mouth and tongue with great vigour and effectiveness. But the areas which are destined to be utilized for the ideational mechanisms of language and reading and writing are unorganized, waiting for the dawn of understanding.

In the early years, even after speech begins, the child's brain continues to be functionally plastic as far as the speech mechanism is concerned. If an infant, who has begun to speak, suffers a large injury to the left hemisphere, he may become dumb for as long as a year. Then he learns again by utilization of homologous areas in the cortex of the right hemisphere. An older child might do this but with increasing difficulty.

On the contrary, however, the adult who receives such a wide-spread injury to the left hemisphere may never succeed in making the transfer, may never speak and read and write again with any degree of perfection. Speech therapy and effort will help repair the defect in inverse ratio to the extent of the lesion. Capacity of substitution of one hemisphere for the other is truly amazing during infancy. But, once functional localization of acquired skills has been established, the early plasticity tends to disappear.

Some of these physiological and anatomical facts that I have discussed in brief outline are new. But many of them have been common knowledge since Broca (1861) first declared that speech had a localized representation in the brain.

It is obvious that the little child, learning to speak his mother's tongue, does so without accent and without apparent effort. When he learns words he is learning about life. Language provides him with a way of asking for, and usually getting, what he wants; a way to share the exciting ideas, that teem in his new-born imagination, with others who love him; a way of understanding the intriguing romance of fairy-tale and the equally intriguing mechanisms of steam-engines, dump-trucks, animals and dolls. For him language is a means to an end and not an end in itself.

At first he mispronounces his words and he creates a delight-ful "lingo" of baby-talk. But all too soon, perhaps, he drops these mispronunciations and adopts the less interesting way of talking used by the adults about him. The mother's method of teaching language is amazingly efficient!

If, before the age of ten to fourteen, the child associates with those who speak a second and even a third language, he can learn by a similar technique two or three languages with no evident increase in his effort.

I had the opportunity of watching this experiment carried out in my own home. Two of our children spoke German in the nursery with a German governess from the beginning. Then, when they first went to school it was to a French nursery school at the ages of three and four. There, work and play were presented to them in the French tongue.

In the nursery with the governess it seemed to them quite natural that the word for dog was "hund." In the nursery school it was "chien" and when they were with their parents it was "dog." There was no confusion, no extra effort, no foreign accents. The change in environment was sufficient to change the way of expression. Or the appearance of the governess who never spoke anything but German might have the same result. The parents also spoke German to the best of their ability in the nursery. This established what may be considered a conditioned reflex.

The experiment was successful. Even the two older children who had played with German children for only a few months at the ages of nine and ten continued to talk with the German governess who entered the family at that time. In each case fluent command of the language was achieved without labour, and the ability has since served useful purposes to three of the four children.

Compare that with the experience of their parents who learned English at home in the usual way and, later, between the ages of sixteen and twenty-two, according to accepted school curricula, studied French and German with Latin and a smattering of Greek thrown in. Still later, Spanish was taken up for a special purpose by the excellent Berlitz method. It was all done with textbooks and word lists and rules of grammar and syntax – homework, toil, trouble and headache.

All this was hard work. The time required was great. The discipline was said to be good for the character. But if the object of it all was to speak easily without accent, to understand quickly and to think in these other languages, the result was certainly a failure.

What happens to the brain when multiple languages are learned? This is an interesting question. Is a separate neurone mechanism for each language set up in different speech areas of the cortex? My answer would be unequivocally "no."

Cases have been reported and published in which injury to the dominant hemisphere has resulted in the loss of one language and the preservation of another. If this claim were substantiated, one would be forced to assume that one area of cortex was used for French and another for Spanish. It is my opinion that careful study of these cases of aphasia would always show involvement of all the languages that have been mastered.

For twenty-five years I have lived and worked in a bilingual society in the Province of Quebec. Many patients speak French and English, often quite fluently. More than once I have heard from an assistant, who was well versed in the published literature of this subject, that an aphasic patient could speak French but was aphasic in English or vice versa. On critical examination it always developed that both languages were involved in the speech defect.

It is characteristic of certain types of aphasia that some words are lost and others retained. Sometimes one or more words are used over and over again. This may be done even when they fail to convey the speaker's meaning. A man may say "yes" when he wants to say "yes" but he continues, to his great chagrin, to say "yes" when he wants to say "no." He has lost the ability to say "no" and he can do no better in French, for he can say neither "oui" nor "non."

When more than one language is learned, the speech areas of the dominant hemisphere take them all on without geographical separation that one can discover. If languages are learned in the right way, and particularly if they are learned at the right age, multiple languages may be learned perfectly, with little effort and without physiological confusion.

It has been said that an educated Englishman or American need not bother with other tongues. From the usual practical point of view this is no doubt quite true. The little-educated man and the university graduate get along, each with his mother tongue alone, quite well enough under ordinary circumstances. They may have no urge to travel for pleasure, profit or interest. They may not care to read current publications in other languages.

But there are many also who feel the urge to travel and read and who are not prepared for it by the schooling of the present day. There are many who believe, as I do, that it is above all the bar of ignorance of language that shuts us off from other peoples, raising as it does a wall about our knowledge and understanding and brotherhood, far more impenetrable than distance or iron curtains.

It has long been one of the avowed objects of education to learn from other cultures. It has been agreed that this could best be done by speaking and reading the language of those other cultures. Hence the standard school exercises in Latin and Greek and in modern language. The problem is a very old one and it was not always solved in the same way.

I spoke of the discovery of writing in Sumer five thousand years and more ago. Semitic conquerors soon came into Sumer speaking a language which we may call Babylonian. They were warlike and untutored. They had much to learn from the more ancient civilization of Sumer. The temple libraries of that land and in that period were filled with clay tablets written in the Sumerian tongue.

Gradually, the common language in city and country came to be Babylonian, but contracts, decisions at law and bills of sale were still invariably written in Sumerian. Educated people understood both tongues.

Thousands of years later, Rome sent out her legions and conquered the world, but Romans had much to learn from Greek culture and their educated people came to know both tongues. Barbarians in northern Europe, among them the ancestors of some of us, threw off the domination of Rome. But, through the dark ages that followed, a scattered few, chiefly in the monasteries and castles, kept the Roman language alive and through it ran a slender stream of knowledge from the past until, at last, the day of the Renaissance dawned. Then Roman law, Greek thought and Hebrew religion burst into a new growth and the way was prepared for the birth of something quite new, Modern Science.

But times have changed and with them the learning of secondary language. The Babylonian once bought a Sumerian slave to teach his children, at an early age, a tongue that would be useful to them when they grew up to become priests, merchants, courtiers. Two thousand years later Roman families of the better class had Greek slaves and much-respected Greek tutors.

In more recent times, governesses and maids who spoke foreign tongues could be hired, and this may well be possible in some parts of the world still. But slavery is gone and domestic servants seem to be fast disappearing on this continent.

The time has come to establish new methods of learning the secondary languages. Ignorance of foreign tongues cuts us off from the rest of the world and from the culture of other lands, which is just as important now as it ever was. To make up for this, foreign languages are taught in the final years of school and college. This is good but the effort yields a surprisingly small return.

I know quite well that educators are not in the habit of asking for physiological consultation in the planning of their curricula, and that the neurosurgeon who offers advice, unasked, may well be placing his head in the lion's mouth. This metaphor is particularly suitable since I am speaking in this venerable Academy of Arts and Sciences, and in Boston where almost everyone is an educator in one field or another.

It may be that the good Lord intended the educated man to read foreign languages painfully and by the sweat of his brow, as a sort of penance, regardless of how easily he learned to manage the mother tongue.

But one who considers only the physiology of the human brain might suggest that a few schools, at least, should be organized somewhat as follows:

Suppose the school which we are to discuss is a day-school in an English-speaking community. Let the first years, from nursery school and kindergarten on to grades for children of eight or ten, be conducted by foreign-born teachers who will speak only their native tongue in school, at work and at organized play.

If such a school is staffed, for example, by German and French teachers, and I make no plea for any particular language, let the little ones begin their years of normal play, drawing, singing and memorizing, in French or German. Teach them no language as such except by the methods so long employed by mother and nursemaid. After, possibly, two years in the French department, let them shift to the German department or vice versa.

Get on from fairy-tales to folk literature as rapidly as the child's mind is prepared for it. These children will have been hearing Mother Goose and such things at home, and their play at the week-ends, as well as the home discipline, will have been carried out in English. In their holidays they will, no doubt, speak English.

Then, at the age of eight to ten, let the children take up mathematics, history and all the other subjects that should be mastered, including the dead languages as desired. This later stage may well be conducted in English with occasional exercises in French or German literature and conversation. They will then be able to pronounce their words and to concern themselves with the content of what they read.

During the first stage of education they will be learning to talk and to read and write. If this stage is properly handled the child will come through it with no more effort than when he learns one language instead of two or three.

I make no pretence to knowledge of the best organization of such a school. My plea is that we should let children hear secondary languages, properly spoken, at an early age. On this continent we are shut off from easy contact with the rest of the world, and it is necessary to give some thought to how we may make ourselves good citizens of the world as well as good Americans, good Canadians, good Englishmen.

I realize that there may be exceptional men, capable of learning language quickly at any age. There are always exceptions. It may be that such men, learning a language late in life, can speak without accent, although I doubt it. There is a good deal of evidence that he who learns more than one language as a little child has greater facility for the acquisition of additional languages in adult life.

The objection has been made that if a person learns a secondary language quite early, it may be completely forgotten with lack of practice. But let such a person live for a few weeks in the country where that language is spoken and he will discover that his former ability has not been lost, nor the skill of pronunciation either.

The duration of man's childhood is very long as compared with that of other animals and the early years are normally devoted to learning a language as a means of learning about life. The human brain has a plasticity at that time and a specialized capacity for acquiring speech which is lost later. Perhaps we who glory in the power of adult reason and who have responsibility for teaching the young, might give some thought to the unalterable evolution of functional specialization in this brain of ours.

When we consider its complexity, composed as it is of thousands of millions of living nerve cells, each sending out or passing on individual electrical currents over insulated wire-like branches, it does seem an unbelievable, a fabulous structure. It can even be used, as now, for self-contemplation.

The brain of man is the organ of destiny. It holds within its humming mechanisms secrets that will determine the future of the human race. Speech might be called the human brain's first miracle. Speech it was that served to make man what he is, instead of one of the animals.

The brain is a living mechanism, not a machine. In case of breakdown, it can substitute one of its parts for the function of another. But it has its limitations. It is subject to inexorable change with the passage of time. It is especially adapted to the learning of language at one stage and to the use of language in reasoned thought at another, a later stage.

"To everything there is a season and a time to every purpose under heaven." Educators, before all others, must realize that this is particularly true of the "organ of the mind." Physiological evolution causes it to specialize in the learning of language first. In regard to this function, it is soon senescent. But it is ready for life's fulfilment in other directions, ready for reasoning, self-discipline, understanding, even wisdom.

Learning a Second Language

[THIRTEEN]

"I have long wondered about secondary education, regarding it from the safe distance of a neurological clinic. I have wondered why the curriculum was not adjusted to the evolution of functional capacity in the brain . . ."

This was the beginning of a talk that I gave to the boys of the final year at Lower Canada College. That was in December 1939. Even at that time, I had begun to study speech disorders and the neurology of language. In 1947, Dr. Lamar Roberts joined me in a planned investigation, and our conclusions were summarized finally in a book [*Speech and Brain-Mechanisms*, 1959, Princeton University Press]. The last chapter of the book was devoted to language-learning from the point of view of language teachers and of parents. I now propose to make informal use of some of this material. Parents can bring up their children to be fluently bilingual or trilingual if they make the effort at the right time. I am convinced also that Canadian schools could do the same with little or no added cost, after a change of system had been inaugurated.

I suppose it may be more convenient, for those whose task it is to plan school curricula, to postpone the teaching of secondary language until the second decade of the child's life. But if their plan does not produce fluency, let them look more carefully at the time-table of the cerebral hemispheres and consider the mother's method of teaching. Every parent and teacher knows that there is a time-table of change that runs through childhood and youth. This time-table is determined in part by

FROM AN ADDRESS TO THE WOMEN'S CANADIAN CLUB, MONTREAL; NOVEMBER 1958.

the growth and evolution of the glands within the body. But there is also a time-table, or a biological clock, of the brain. It must not be overlooked.

Suppose a government, seeking to combat overpopulation, were to pass a law that marriage must wait until the age of forty. What solution could be more logical? And the plan might well succeed if only men and women were machines instead of the living, growing, changing creatures that they are. Such a law, you may well exclaim, would be contrary to the unfolding nature of men and women. But I say the same is true of a school curriculum in which the teaching of secondary language makes its first appearance at twelve or sixteen years of age.

In the beginning, before he speaks, a child learns to know the meaning of the objects about him. Animals do the same. He understands certain concepts – going out of doors, eating, and so on – from experience. Animals do the same and somewhat more rapidly. The child learns to understand the names for simple concepts. Animals follow him there, too, a little way.

But when the child begins to speak, the animal is blocked; he can no longer follow. This is to be explained by the fact that there are, in the human brain, new and larger areas which are not present in the brains of other animals. There are specialized convolutions which, because of their connections, can be devoted to the understanding of speech and to the use of speech. One may assume, hypothetically of course, that when these new evolutionary enlargements of the brain made their appearance, far off in the distant past, man began to talk.

From that distant day onward, women taught their children to speak. Here is where mothers make their great contribution to the destiny of the race. The mother's method is amazingly efficient. Impelled by that strange force, mother love, she talks and smiles into the little face and talks again, waiting wisely, using baby-talk, and at last, after a year of waiting perhaps, the baby speaks and she witnesses again the miracle that makes man what he is and lifts him above the beasts. But her work goes on until the child has acquired the basic units of her language.

The teaching of the mother tongue by the mother is carried out by what we may call the *direct method*. It has also been used successfully by servants and occasional tutors in the home to teach one, two or more secondary languages from the dawn of history. This makes it all the more surprising that educators today do not generally employ the method in schools. Perhaps there is a general expectation that new methods will be better than old.

The teaching of a secondary language in school by means of the standard technique of word lists, and grammar and syntax, is the *indirect method*. This indirect method was borrowed from the techniques of teaching dead languages such as Sanskrit, Latin, and Greek. Application of such a method to a living language is an innovation introduced by educators in comparatively recent times.

There are two reasons for the success of the mother's direct method. First, of course, is the age of the child. But there is a second reason which is psychological. This is something that may easily be overlooked. For the child, the learning of language is a method of learning about life, a means of getting what he wants, a way of satisfying the curiosity that burns in him almost from the beginning. Here is the psychological advantage.

The direct method of learning language can succeed at an older age, even after nine years, and adults can of course learn by it, as shown in the success of the Berlitz method.

Take the case of Josef Konrad Korzeniowski as an example of triple language-learning by the direct method. He was a Polish boy and yet he became a master of the English language, second only to Shakespeare, perhaps. As a British subject and a celebrated author, he was known as Joseph Conrad. English was for him a tertiary language. Polish was his mother's tongue but he spoke French as a child with his nursery governess. Then he sailed away on a British ship at the age of fifteen years.

At sea he heard no other language than English, and so began to learn this language by the "mother's method." He learned the "lingo" and the slang first, no doubt. The psychology of language-learning, in this sailing-ship, was like that in the home. There was no translating. He pronounced words wrongly first as a baby does but kept on improving the sounds until they corresponded with the words the sailors used, and later with the sounds that cultured people make. English words were the immediate symbols through which he must come to understand life. They were the symbols that brought him food and success as a young sailor. Thus, he learned the sort of language he would never have discovered, however hard he might have worked, with dictionary and grammar as his only guide. He learned the good, short, simple words and the speech that men use in the face of trial and danger.

"Goodbye brothers," he wrote, "you were a good crowd. As good a crowd as ever fisted with wild cries the beating canvas of a heavy foresail; or tossing aloft, invisible in the night, gave back yell for yell to a westerly gale."

I have been told by one who knew Conrad after Conrad had become a famous author in England, that he spoke English beautifully. He recalls now no obvious accent in the author's speech.

At Yale University, Gesell and Ilg have studied a large series of unilingual children. Leopold, on the other hand, made an exhaustive ten-year study of his own two children who were brought up in his completely bilingual family. From such studies it is possible to write out the time-table of household teaching and learning. During the infant's first year he begins to coo and then to babble. Babbling, we are told, is verbal play with sounds at the front of the mouth and clear consonants. The first word is usually spoken about the time of the first birthday. In the second year he learns to understand first and later to speak.

According to Leopold, there is apt to be a lag, during this early period, between the first hearing of words and their first utterance – a lag of two to seven months. Between the ages of two and four years, the child perfects his pronunciation, and the baby-talk, which is such a delight to parents, disappears.

Dr. Ilg, in her study of language-learning, recognizes two types of child. The one she calls imitative and the other creative. The imitative child learns more rapidly and accurately, with less baby-talk and jargon. Girls are more likely to be placed in this group of accurate learners than are boys. In the second group, the creative learner is slower to make progress. He is more apt to elaborate a pronunciation and a jargon of his own. Poets, Ilg says, are prone to come from this second group!

Capacity for imitation is maximum between the ages of four

and eight. It decreases steadily throughout later childhood. The first language is well set by the age of four or five, and by the age of six to eight years the child has formed his native speech-habits completely. They are not yet so firmly established, how-ever, as to interfere with his capacity to acquire a second lan-guage without translation.

Now, here is the essential element in direct teaching and learning. There is little or no translation. This is possible if the age is young and if the method is right. Conrad learned Polish and French concurrently from infancy, and learned English beginning at fifteen. But since he did so without any transla-tion, the method was direct in each case.

Some professional educators have made the statement that it is psychologically bad for children to begin a second language before the first is well fixed. They fear that there may be con-flicts. This view is, I believe, in error. There are other reasons for conflicts and for the appearance of "problem children," whether one or more languages are being learned.

If one person always speaks French to a child and another always speaks English, he turns spontaneously from one language to the other in addressing them. It becomes a condi-tioned reflex. There is no conflict. There is no added labour, no increased work. Two or three languages present no greater problem to the child than a single language. But, this does seem to present a greater problem to the would-be analyst!

If your child, who has learned English at home, comes under the direction of a teacher who speaks only French at school or on the playground, he will soon accept the fact that in the presence of that teacher the words to be used in order to do well in a game or competition or task are different from the words that he must use in the presence of English-speaking teachers. It should be as simple as that.

On the other hand, if he is taught a language by the secondary method, by a teacher who speaks to him in English while teach-ing French, then he must translate. It may seem simple to teacher and analyst. But the child faces one of the really great problems and difficulties of formal education.

The time to begin what might be called a general schooling in secondary languages in accordance with the demands of brain capacity and normal psychology is between four and ten. The child sets off for school then, and he can still learn new languages without interposing the speech units of his mother tongue.

Consider the experience of any immigrant family in a new country. Suppose the family is not subjected to any school-teaching. Within a year or two, the children will have learned the language of the country to which they have come, and they will speak it without accent. They may even serve as interpreters for their parents. The parents will learn too. But they will speak the language with considerable effort and with a marked accent. The parents will interpose the firmly established units of their native tongue between the thought and the words of the new language. They will translate, whereas the child will imitate and develop new units in the new language by the direct method.

The same area of cerebral cortex which is used for a store-house of English is used also for French or Chinese or any language. There is no displacement of one language area from another, that we can discover. There is, however, the very efficient switch-over mechanism from one language system to another language system.

I have quoted the conclusion of Leopold concerning the second year of a child's life. There is a lag, he says, of from two to seven months after the first hearing of a word at that period and before its first meaningful utterance. When the child speaks he will imitate the sound of some phrase like "go bye-bye" in a voluntary act, probably making one word out of it, perhaps something like "bye." Having spoken, he will repeat that word often. Each time he hears his mother say it in the next few months he will probably say it after her and gradually improve his pronunciation. Thus he will make for himself a unit within the brain for the recognition of that sound and a unit for expressing the sound. Both units depend upon the new speech convolutions of the left hemisphere.

As time passes, the child is able to acquire units of under-standing, and units of speaking, faster and faster. By the time he can pronounce a few hundred words accurately, he uses those units for rapid expansion of vocabulary. His accent has been set. He no longer experiments with sounds.

At eight or nine he enters gradually into a new period. Mathematics are easy for him. New words and new knowledge are acquired rapidly and he is apt to read widely, hungrily. This is good. The speech mechanism is using the units already acquired and adds new words with great speed. But it is becoming rigid and resistant toward the beginning of a new language. All new words are pronounced with accents he has learned earlier and his sentence construction is fixed by the well-known phrases and basic words first acquired. He passes from the earlier plastic period into the rigid adult period, from the earlier period of unit formation into the period of vocabulary expansion.

Now, if the child has been exposed by parent or playmate to a second and a third language, or if he has had teachers with native accents during the early period, he has acquired the basic units of those languages and preserves them within his brain. This makes vocabulary expansion at any later period easy, with rapid learning and a good accent.

I have heard it said that there is little profit in exposing English children to another language if they live on in an English community. They will forget all their words. That is true. But if they study the language, whether French or German or Russian, later on in school or college, or if they go to that foreign country, they will, I believe, discover an unsuspected gift of language-learning. Their basic units are not lost.

Many can testify to this. My elder son was in Madrid with us at the age of five while I was studying with Ramón y Cajal, the great anatomist of the brain. My wife walked back and forth each day, or took the tramway, to put him in a Spanish school for a period of three months. No one taught him Spanish as such. He enjoyed the games at school, if he did not enjoy it when the occasional stick was thrown at the little foreigner and his toddling sister. At about the age of thirty, it became necessary for him to learn Spanish for business purposes. He thought he knew nothing of it. But unexpected pronunciations came echoing back from a forgotten past and formed a basic currency that brought rapid progress. The word for streetcar which any

Canadian would call "tramvia" he pronounced something like "thramvia"; Madrid was something like "Mothre." I do not pronounce the words properly, having learned to speak poor Spanish at thirty-three without his early conditioning. (I had heard no Spanish previously, nor French, nor German before the age of eighteen; only Latin!) Units of understanding as well as units of pronunciation were hidden away in his brain, forgotten but not lost.

I have heard statements like the following: "Some men have a genius for learning new languages. Others have not, and that is all there is to it. The English cannot learn secondary languages. The Dutch and Poles and the Swiss learn without half trying. That is just too bad for the English, but there it is."

I suspect that the basic units of second languages are hidden away in the brain during the childhood of those who grow up in lands where many languages echo in playground and home. This it is, perhaps, that makes the Pole and the Swiss and the Hollander better language students. I suspect, further, that the child who has the basic units of French and English hidden away in his brain finds it easier in later life to take up a third language, for example German, even by the indirect method. He has a double number of basic units to call on. And they are similar, at least in part, to those needed.

There are new and promising ventures in language-learning in Ontario. The University of Western Ontario conducts a splendid summer course in Trois Pistoles, Quebec, with excellent opportunities for teen-age students to talk French.

Dr. Robert Gauthier, Director of French Instruction for the Ontario Department of Education, is conducting an experiment based on sound principles of direct language-learning in certain English schools of Ottawa.* I have visited the experiment and have seen a clever French-Canadian teacher in a class of English pupils which he was conducting for one period two or three times a week. He spoke only French during the period and the children were allowed to answer in English or French alternatively without penalty. I visited the classes after five months and found that far more than half of the English children were

---

* Later transferred to Oakville, Ontario.

answering spontaneously and regularly in French, using the teacher's accent. When he tested them, making jokes and purposeful misstatements in French, all of the children laughed.

If the Ontario Department of Education cannot employ enough French teachers to teach kindergarten and the first year or two of school wholly in French, which would be the best method, perhaps they will direct Dr. Gauthier to train twenty-five young French teachers instead of one, in his so-called TAN-GAU method. Then we will see an experiment worth watching, though the word "experiment" should really not be applied to the mother's direct method of teaching a language. That experiment proved to be a success many, many centuries ago.

If schools do nothing about setting up the teaching of secondary languages by the direct method, parents must take the initiative themselves. Get someone who will speak only a foreign tongue to come into the family, or exchange your children for a few months with parents in whose homes another tongue is used, or send them to special schools. Do it in the first decade of life or at least in the first half of the second decade. This will greatly facilitate the teaching of the literature of secondary languages later on in high school and college. I would not suggest that the indirect method of teaching has no place in the later years of education. But certainly it will never make a country bilingual.

I have spoken of language-learning as a physiologist, a parent and a citizen. Here is an executive problem for our educators. Our children are ready to learn secondary languages if you will give them a chance.

When it is learned in the normal physiological way, language need not be taught at all in early stages. It can be learned as a by-product of other pursuits. The learner should understand in the language, speak in the language, think in the language, even ignore the language. For the direct learner, language is not a subject to be studied nor an object to be grasped. It is a means to other ends, a preparation for later study of the literature of that language. Surely the school curriculum can be adjusted to the evolution of functional capacity of the brain – by simple changes in timing and method.

The Physiological Basis of the Mind

[FOURTEEN]

One evening in the late eighteenth century an Italian woman stood in her kitchen watching the frogs' legs which she was preparing for the evening meal. "Look at those muscles moving," she said to her husband. "They always seem to come alive when I hang them on the copper wire."

Her husband looked. He was Professor of Surgery in the University of Bologna but his name is known to us as the discoverer of electricity, Luigi Galvani. Here was the beginning of it all, two hundred years ago. The cut end of the frog's nerve was in contact with the copper wire, and electric current produced by the contact was passing along the nerve to the muscle. As a result, the muscle was twitching and contracting.

Galvani did not understand just where the energy was coming from at first, but nevertheless here, with his wife's help, he had discovered the key to electricity, and to nerve conduction, and to muscle action. Here was the basis of all animal movement, reflex and voluntary, in frog and man. You see, from the time of the Greek physician, Galen, sixteen centuries before Galvani, men had considered that there was a spirit or *anima* within the body that carried mysterious messages to the hand and the foot and the tongue, to move them.

From now on, electric currents were to explain all this – how the frog could jump at the approach of danger, how we can put one foot before the other to walk or run, how we move our mouths and muscles of respiration in order to talk, how we

ADDRESS AT THE SYMPOSIUM ON "MAN AND CIVILIZATION: CONTROL OF THE MIND", UNIVERSITY OF CALIFORNIA SCHOOL OF MEDICINE, SAN FRANCISCO; JANUARY 1961.

move our eyes to read, how we turn our heads to listen. But they did not explain how the frog came to be aware of danger, nor do they answer the riddle of how we think. That is what you have asked me to explain at the start of this symposium!

All these body movements, some of them subject to the will and others quite involuntary, are executed as motor mechanisms initiated by electrical potentials that flash out along the nerves to the muscles and from the muscles back again to the central nervous system which is housed within the spinal cord and the brain. More than that, we know now that it is electrical potentials which speed from the sense organs – the eye, the ear, the nose, the tongue and the skin – inward along the nerves to the brain. All sensory information from our bodies and from the world around us becomes available within the brain.

Thus, neurophysiology has explained away the mysterious *anima*, the spirit of ancient days, quite successfully. But what about the remaining intangibles, the mind and consciousness and the soul? No, these things science has not explained. So far, one conclusion seems clear to neurophysiologists: There is no evidence of any mental activity unless some action is going on in the brain.

Brain action consists in the travelling of electrical potentials along circuits formed by nerve-fibre bundles within the brain. The nerve fibres are branches from living nerve cells which form the grey matter of the brain. The grey matter is found in nuclear collections within the centre of the brain, and it forms the cerebral cortex that covers the hemispheres. There are said to be twelve billion nerve cells (neurones) in one human brain. The branching nerve fibres that issue from them are capable of conducting currents, and each of these cells is capable of producing a small amount of electrical energy within itself. That energy can boost or block or alter the currents that would pass and re-pass along its fibres.

Sir Charles Sherrington, my teacher in undergraduate and graduate years at Oxford, was a great leader of neurophysiologists in his time. Here is a description he gave of man's nervous system, to a lay audience. It betrays the fact that he was really a poet as well as a scientist.

"Picture to yourself," he said, "a scheme of lines and nodal points gathered together at one end into a great ravelled knot, the brain, and at the other trailing off to a sort of stalk, the spinal cord. Imagine activity shown in this by little points of light. Of these some, stationary, flash rhythmically, faster or slower. Others are travelling points streaming in serial lines at various speeds. The rhythmic stationary lights lie at the nodes. The nodes are both goals whither converge, and junctions whence diverge, the lines of travelling lights. Suppose we choose the hour of deep sleep. Then only in some sparse and out-of-the-way places are nodes flashing and trains of light-points running. The great knotted headpiece lies for the most part quite dark. Occasionally at places in it lighted points flash or move but soon subside.

"Should we continue to watch the scheme we should observe after a time an impressive change which suddenly accrues. In the great head end which had been mostly darkness spring up myriads of lights, as though activity from one of these local places suddenly spread far and wide. The great topmost sheet of the mass, where hardly a light had twinkled or moved, becomes now a sparkling field of rhythmic flashing points, with trains of travelling sparks hurrying hither and thither. It is as if the Milky Way entered upon some cosmic dance. Swiftly the head mass becomes an enchanted loom where millions of flashing shuttles weave a dissolving pattern, always a meaningful pattern though never an abiding one. The brain is waking and with it the mind is returning."

It was in 1950 that I was first invited to take part in a symposium-discussion of the brain and the mind. That was a B.B.C. series of broadcasts entitled: *The Physical Basis of Mind*. Scientists and philosophers took part in it.* The scientists were all physicians – two physiologists, two anatomists, a psychiatrist, a neurologist and a neurosurgeon. They spoke first and the three philosophers last so they could listen, if they thought it worth while, to what the physicians said week by week before their turns should come.

The symposium was opened by Sherrington who was ninety-three in that year. At the close of his talk he chuckled and

---

* *The Physical Basis of Mind,* ed. Peter Laslett. Oxford: Blackwell, 1950.

remarked that, two thousand years ago, Aristotle "was asking how the mind is attached to the body."

Let me turn now to the reports of the philosophers. Perhaps this may be as good a way as any other to let you see the problem of neurophysiology from without. A. J. Ayer, Professor of Philosophy in University College, London, quoted from the broadcast which Adrian, a physiologist from Cambridge, had made:

"The part of the picture of the brain which may always be missing," Adrian had said, "is, of course, the part which deals with the mind, the part which ought to explain how a particular pattern of nerve impulses can produce an idea: Or the other way round, how a thought can decide which nerve cells are to come into action."

Ayer then asserted that if people would only abandon the ancient thinking of Descartes that mind and body are separate, the problem would become a philosophical one, and no longer be a matter of scientific concern.

"The picture we are given" (by the scientists), he continued, "is that of messengers travelling through the brain, reaching a mysterious entity called the mind, receiving orders from it, and then travelling on. But since the mind has no position in space – it is by definition not the sort of thing that can have position in space – it does not literally make sense to talk of physical signals reaching it."

How logical this philosopher's approach to the problem seems! And how impressively like the method of Socrates! Socrates used to leave his embarrassed pupils to find their own way out of a situation that he had shown to be absurd. But in this case the neurophysiologists already recognize the nature of the inconsistency. Therein lies the problem.

The "messages travelling through the brain" never do reach a place that we can discover where the mind is found. Say rather that electrical currents pass through differing circuits of the brain and that there is simultaneous change in the shapes of conscious thought. The passing of potentials and the concomitant change of thought are apparently identical in time, but there is no meeting as far as we can determine. We are beginning to learn where the brain action is, but we know no "where" of mind. Nor can we see, as yet, that either one comes first, the change in thought or the movement of current. The riddle we must try to solve is this: What is the nature of the mind? How is it joined to action within the brain? To declare that these things are one, not two, does not make them so. But it does block the progress of research.

Gilbert Ryle, the Professor of Metaphysical Philosophy at Oxford, employed amused sarcasm rather than Socratic logic in his contribution to the symposium. It ended with this sweeping injunction:

"The umbrella titles 'Mind' and 'Matter' obliterate the very differences that ought to interest us. Theorists should drop both these words.

" 'Mind' and 'Matter' are echoes . . ." of the arguments of the philosophy of the past.

Neither of these philosophers suggested what words we should use when we talk with the men and women whose brain-mind or mind-brain problem we must continue to study. They did not trouble to advise us frankly whether to embrace the gospel of materialism which assumes that all is matter, energy and automatic mechanism. (This would be in keeping with the philosophy of Karl Marx.) Neither did they suggest that we should adopt the ancient preaching of Bishop Berkeley that all is mind. This philosophy echoes still in the gentle teaching of Christian Science. Choosing this side of the shield we might be forced to abandon biological science as unnecessary!

Viscount Samuel, the third philosopher, did give due consideration to the facts. He pointed out that neither the materialist nor the idealist point of view had "won general assent" during the discussion of this problem. "This," he said, "is one of the oldest and most fundamental of the problems of philosophy – the relation between mind and matter. For centuries, philosophers of different schools have made strenuous efforts to resolve one into the other."

"The whole effort," he said, "to resolve mind into matter or else matter into mind is the outcome of what T. H. Green called 'the philosophic craving for unity' . . . An essential duality in nature is the alternative that is left.

"This discussion," Samuel continued, "has helped to clarify

Fig. 1 BLACKBOARD DRAWING: UPPER SKETCH.

Left cerebral hemisphere shown in outline within the head. Streams of electrical potentials are shown as they pass normally from eye and ear and body to the visual, auditory and somatic-sensory areas of the cerebral cortex. The sensory areas are special transmitting platforms. The three streams of current make seeing, hearing and feeling possible. They flow to the cortical platforms and on again down into the thalamus which is part of the brain-stem, as shown in the lower sketch.

BLACKBOARD DRAWING: LOWER SKETCH.

The old brain, or brain-stem, is shown dotted beneath the left hemisphere. The two hemispheres, left and right, are outgrowths from the brain-stem which is said to be "old" because it is present in lower mammals and birds and fishes where hemispheres are little developed. The cerebral hemispheres reach a very high degree of proportional development in man. The streams of sensory input, drawn above, are now shown continuing on from cortex to brain-stem.

Voluntary movement is carried out according to the patterns of the outflowing electrical potentials. This stream arises in the brain-stem, flows outward to the motor gyrus and is then transmitted down through brain-stem, spinal cord and nerves to the muscles.

Between this sensory input, which makes awareness of environment possible, and the motor output controlling conscious behaviour, there is co-ordinating and integrating activity. This takes place in the centrencephalic system, a system of insulated nerve fibres and nerve cells that conduct currents within the brain-stem and out to both hemispheres and back again.

Fig. 2 BLACKBOARD DRAWING: UPPER SKETCH.

Posterior portions of the two hemispheres. The interpretive areas are located on the superior (buried) surface and the lateral surface of both temporal lobes, avoiding the area used for speech. The interpretive area is employed by an individual when comparing the current present experience with the record of non-verbal past experience. The principal area of cortex devoted to speech interpretation and speech formulation is that marked "Ideational Speech" on the dominant hemisphere (usually the left). The secondary speech area (Broca) and supplementary area are not shown here.

BLACKBOARD DRAWING: LOWER SKETCH.

Centrencephalic interconnections are suggested between cerebral cortex and brain-stem. Between sensory input and directed motor output, the circuits of memory and the special areas of cerebral cortex (which are neither sensory nor motor) may be called into action. Such neurone activity may be said to constitute the physical basis of the mind.

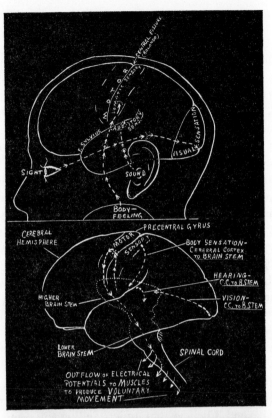

CENTRAL FISSURE (ROLANDO)

M O T O R
SOMATIC SENSORY
AUDITORY SENS.
F. SYLVIUS
VISUAL SENSATION
SIGHT
SOUND
BODY-FEELING

CEREBRAL HEMISPHERE
PRECENTRAL GYRUS
MOTOR
SENSORY
BODY SENSATION-
CEREBRAL CORTEX
TO BRAIN STEM
HEARING-
C.C. TO B.STEM
VISION-
C.C. TO B.STEM
HIGHER BRAIN STEM
LOWER BRAIN STEM
SPINAL CORD
OUTFLOW OF ELECTRICAL POTENTIALS TO MUSCLES TO PRODUCE VOLUNTARY MOVEMENT

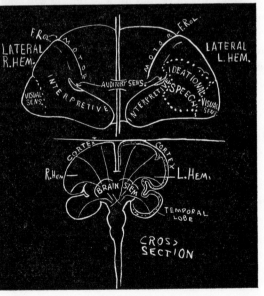

F.ROL.
LATERAL R.HEM.
MOTOR
AUDITORY SENS.
VISUAL SENS.
INTERPRETIVE

F.ROL.
LATERAL L.HEM.
MOTOR
IDEATIONAL SPEECH
VISUAL SENS.
INTERPRETIVE

CORTEX
CORTEX
R.HEM.
BRAIN STEM
L.HEM.
TEMPORAL LOBE

CROSS SECTION

the whole problem by establishing the fact that the meeting-place is not at the points where external stimuli impinge upon the nervous system; it is at the points where mind accepts and utilizes the sense-data offered by the brain. But the discussion has not been able to answer the question what it is that takes over at those points; and therefore it could not even begin to consider how the connection was made."

Then Samuel quoted Sherrington: "That our being should consist of *two* fundamental elements offers, I suppose, no greater inherent improbability than that it should rest on one only." And again, "We have to regard the relation of mind to brain as still not merely unsolved, but still devoid of a basis for its very beginning."

Lord Samuel concluded: "That, it seems, is where we are now: at a standstill. Until science and philosophy can help us to move on from that position we cannot hope that the universe will, for us, be rationalized."

Here in San Francisco in 1961, we must accept this statement still. We have no basis on which to begin to understand the relation of mind to the brain. But the light of science will be brighter as the years pass, cast a wider circle, embrace things that lie beyond. I believe that understanding will come in time, with continued advance – not to us but to our successors.

I should try to tell you, then, where physiology stands in its approach to this hoped-for basis of understanding.

Some of you are physicians. But you may have turned to other interests in medicine. Let me simplify. You will remember your lectures on neuro-anatomy and what you saw in the dissecting room. You were impressed by this great cream-coloured organ separated from the skull by the two mother membranes. First there was the *dura mater*, tough and shining and silver-white, just beneath the bone of the skull, and under that the delicate transparent *pia mater* covering the brain's rounded convolutions and bridging the fissures where you could see the clear cerebrospinal fluid that bathes the brain and floats it as though in a bath within the skull.

You remember the carpet of arteries and veins that nourish the cortex of grey matter so richly, and the drawings of the brain. There was the vertical fissure named for Rolando. The convolution in front of it was labelled *motor* and you were told it controlled the opposite side of the face and the arm and leg. The convolution behind the fissure was marked *sensory* and you knew it had to do with discriminative sensibility on the opposite side of the body; not pain sensation. The inflow of pain sense stopped in the thalamus, deep in the brain, without reaching the cortex.

The occipital lobes at the back of the head were labelled *visual*, and on the edge of the superior convolution of the temporal lobe was the margin of the *auditory* area, most of which was buried in the deep fissure of Sylvius. You were told too that somewhere hidden under the brain were small areas related to the sense of *smell* and also *taste*. On the left hemisphere the word *speech* was written in two places – one on the posterior part of the temporal lobe and one on the lower part of the frontal lobe.

You probably remember that Pavlov showed that removing areas of cerebral cortex made a dog forget what he had learned. Lashley claimed a rat would learn again, no matter which part of the cortex had been removed, as long as some was left. Lashley spent his life looking for the "engram" in the animal brain, the local memory trace, knowing it must be somewhere. He never found it.

In the case of man, physiologists and anatomists were content to follow the sensory tracts from the skin and eye and ear and other sense organs on the outside of the body inward and up to the cortex. Then they followed the motor fibres down from the cortex to the muscles on the opposite side of the body.

The cerebral cortex, they assumed, was the end and the beginning, the top, the mysterious place where Mind might possibly have its existence like the gods on Mount Olympus. What happened between sensory arrival at the cortex and motor emission was a mystery. Neurologists talked vaguely of "association" fibres that did something by connecting the nerve cells of the cortex with each other.

Let me make an addition to that picture, an addition that is partly hypothesis and partly proven. First, the sensory pathways do not end on the cortex. The high road of elaborative sensory conduction goes to cortex and then returns directly into the thalamic centres – where the pain pathway had ended directly, without such a detour to the cortex. Pain is the same for man and snake and you might consider that man has no pain area in cerebral cortex because there is no need of elaboration of that sensation in the human cortex. Reflex jerking away of the injured part is sufficient.

Secondly, the stream of electrical impulses that controls the voluntary muscles does not begin in the cortex. It begins somewhere near where the sensory tracts seem to end, in the underlying brain-stem. From the brain-stem, it flows out to the motor gyrus of the cortex on both sides and then on to the muscles.

Thirdly, there must be, in what we may call the higher portion of the brain-stem, a system of nerve tracts and cell collections which are connected symmetrically with the cerebral cortex on either side. Many of these connections, like the stems of lily pads, provide the cortex with functional control and connection.

Now let us turn to the mental processes which are called perception, memory of past experience, memory of words, memory of concepts, interpretation of present experience, the directing and focusing of attention that selects and excludes material for thought, decision of action. All those things, those psychological processes, must be subserved by the co-ordinating and integrating currents that pass over the connections of this central system. If there is truly a neuronal mechanism that serves effectively as the basis of conscious thought, the mechanism must use these paths.

When there is damage to, or interference with, the higher brain-stem, whether due to indirect concussion or direct injury, or tumour pressure, or vascular "stroke," the result is inevitably the loss of consciousness. If the neuronal activity which co-ordinates and integrates brain action and makes conscious thought possible takes place here, then this loss of consciousness is to be expected. On the other hand, large areas of cortex can be removed on one or both sides without loss of consciousness.

These connections that pass through the higher brain-stem and unite the two hemispheres and which seem to be indispensable for conscious thinking may be called the *centren-*

cephalic system. Some of the pathways are known and many only surmised.

Do not jump to the conclusion that I am suggesting the brain-stem to be the location of an entity called mind or consciousness. One distinguished neurologist has already made that mistake and wasted some breath on it. That would be just as erroneous as to suggest that consciousness sits in the cortex or that it has a position in space anywhere. What we may assume is this:

The functional action going on in some part of the cortex of one or both hemispheres, together with some part of the brain-stem makes possible conscious mental processes or states of mind. It is through the centrencephalic system of connections that the co-ordination of brain action is carried out.

In 1953 I took part in a second symposium on the brain-mind problem. It was called the "Laurentian Symposium" on *Brain Mechanisms and Consciousness.* This time the discussants were all physicians coming from various parts of the world, including Professor Donald Hebb, who will speak to us this afternoon. Some progress was made, as compared with the 1950 symposium, partly due to the fact that the reticular activating system, a system of connecting fibres, had been recently discovered in the brain and those responsible for this discovery were present: Moruzzi (Pisa) and Magoun (Los Angeles) and Morison (Harvard).

Adrian (Cambridge), who was present again, pointed out that this system of connections not only seems to control the general level of vigilance of the cerebral cortex but also probably has "something to do with the direction of attention, with the actual work of the conscious brain." Let me turn now to our present symposium.

Hughlings Jackson, a nineteenth-century neurologist, stated long ago that "There is no such entity as consciousness; we are from moment to moment differently conscious." Corresponding with these differences that Jackson had in mind, we must assume that the circuits of the integrating system are differently employed. We are differently conscious, no doubt, because different circuits of the brain-stem and different areas of the cerebral cortex are activated by the "rhythmic flashing points with trains of travelling sparks hurrying hither and thither" that Sherrington described.

Time was when the brain was considered to be the "organ of the mind" functioning as a whole during all conscious states. Such a point of view is no longer tenable. Modern advances in knowledge lead us to ever-increasing localization of function within the brain. We are differently conscious from moment to moment, and concomitant with that there is a differing pattern of neurone activity.

When a man is using words, for example – it may be during speech or writing, or listening to speech, or reading or indeed at times when words are used in quiet thinking – there must always be utilization of the speech areas in the left cerebral cortex and in the underlying posterior thalamic nucleus of the left, the dominant, hemisphere. However, a man can play the piano with both hands or drive a car or understand the nature of an experience without calling on that speech mechanism at all.

As a neurosurgeon, I have found it necessary, as many neuro-surgeons have, to remove large areas of cerebral cortex on one side, from a patient while he was still conscious, using local anaesthesia. As long as the brain-stem is not molested, the patient remains conscious and, curiously enough, he is not aware of any change until he turns his attention to a proposi-tion that calls for specific use of the removed portion of his cerebral cortex. Then he may discover, for example, that he cannot feel accurately what he touches with the left hand or that, although he still sees to the right, he no longer sees objects on the left. (These are not experiments but part of some procedure being carried on for urgent treatment.)

Jung of Freiburg has urged that the essential element in consciousness is the focusing of attention, the selecting of cer-tain things as though a beam of light were focused upon them. I like this emphasis because it gives the neurophysiologist some-thing to search for – the directional mechanism of attention. It suggests that the origin of the figurative beam of light is situated in the higher brain-stem. But brain action takes place in both regions (brain-stem and the selected area of cortex) working together. To focus his attention, a man somehow selects certain circuits of the brain, and activates them.

Now let me turn for a moment to some of the faculties of the mind. Take memory, for example, which has its different forms. It may be shown that man has a functionally separable neuronal mechanism for 1) memory of current experience, 2) memory of words, 3) memory of generalizations or concepts. These separations may be demonstrated occasionally on the operating table when the patient is fully conscious and the brain is exposed.

A large part of the grey matter that covers the temporal lobe may be called interpretive cortex. Functionally it may be considered to belong to a different integrative level than the so-called sensory cortex and motor cortex because it deals with the records of experiences that have already passed through the mind. When a gentle electric current is applied to this area of cortex the patient may, for example, exclaim suddenly, "I hear my mother and brother talking." (In that particular case, when the surgeon stopped and asked, the patient explained that they were in the living-room at home and she seemed to be there with them, seeing and hearing the same things that she heard and saw in some past strip of time. And yet, at the same time, she was aware of the fact that she was in the operating room on the operating table.)

Many different past experiences have been recalled thus by the electrode, sometimes from a recent, and sometimes from a far distant past. For example, the recall may have summoned a time of listening to an orchestra, a time of hearing and seeing a man at the piano in a café, a time of laughing conversation with friends, a time of standing on the street corner at "Jacob and Worthington, South Bend, Indiana," a time of lying in the delivery room at childbirth, and many other personal experiences.

These flashbacks carry far more detail than any person could summon voluntarily. Sometimes, instead of this type of experiential recall, the patient makes a sudden re-interpretation of the present time and situation, a false interpretation. For example, he may say suddenly, "I feel as though this had all happened before"; or "I am afraid," as though the environment were all at once threatening.

We conclude that, in the interpretive cortex, it is possible to activate electrically a functional unit that operates under normal conditions as a subconscious reflex. You have all had the sudden feeling of familiarity. After this reflex signal, a bit of your own past comes back. It is apparent that in any normal individual, when the present experience resembles strikingly an experience from the past, that past is summoned reflexly, automatically. A man is not aware of the summoning until the interpretation, for example, that the situation is familiar or dangerous, flashes up in consciousness. That happens even before the similar recollection can be identified. Presently, the subject discovers that the data from the past has come within voluntary reach. The man or the place you saw last perhaps fifteen years ago comes back to you sufficiently to make you aware of the changes time has wrought.

Here is a unitary functional mechanism that is located in the cortex at least in part. This is the record of the things that were once within the spotlight of a man's attention, not the things he ignored but the things he was aware of in a previous period of time. The trace or engram or neurone record is not located in temporal cortex, I suspect, but is at a distance, where it can be reached and activated from the cortex. Exactly where, we cannot yet be quite sure.

Speech, likewise, has a separable mechanism. In this case, the electric current can be used in a different way, to paralyse, rather than to activate. The cortical speech mechanism may be blocked selectively when an electrode is placed on a speech convolution. The current interferes with its use, but the patient is not aware of this interference unless he happens to want to speak. Then he discovers to his astonishment that he cannot capture words. One patient was being shown a picture of a butterfly when the electrode was applied to the speech area. He was silent. After the electrode had been withdrawn he explained that he could not get the word "butterfly" so he tried for moth. But that word, too, would not come.

Thus, it is apparent that his capacity to recognize and perceive the nature of the object shown him was intact. The memories of the concept of butterfly and the concept of moth were also intact. Somehow, within the circuits that form the basis of the mind, he had presented those concepts, one after the other, to the speech mechanism with a negative result. Here is an example of the operation of the mind. Action in the brain accompanied the thought part way, but when words were called for, the brain failed. The patient expected an automatic response, expected the word to flash up in consciousness reflexly. It was not that his lips and tongue were paralysed. It was the idea of the word that was not forthcoming.

There are, as you see, many demonstrable mechanisms. They work for the purposes of the mind automatically when called upon. These mechanisms – those that we have begun to understand – constitute part, at least, of the *physiological basis of the mind*. But what agency is it that calls upon these mechanisms, choosing one rather than another? Is it another mechanism or is there in the mind something of different essence?

Here we have come to what Samuel called the "meeting-place." We may not call it a place, and yet we grope our way back to the idea of the *neighbourhood of brain action*. This is as far as science can carry us now. It will go farther in the years to come, much farther; and I believe, though I cannot prove it, that the truth which we "know in part" will be revealed in full to man through man's continuing effort. Some day "the universe will for us be rationalized."

Surely we are nearer the goal than Aristotle was and yet, after all this progress, when we try to see the actual link between the patterning of electrical impulses in the brain and a change in the mind of man, we are still in the dark – as much in the dark as Aristotle when he asked so long ago, "How is the mind attached to the body?"

In conclusion, it must be said that there is as yet no scientific proof that the brain can control the mind, or fully explain the mind. The assumptions of materialism have never been substantiated. Those who study the brain can only carry on, observing its mechanisms with an open mind. They must strive to prove how nerve impulse and thought could be one, or on the other hand to discover the nature of mind as a separate element and so make dualism scientific. I suspect that when men see this problem more clearly they will discover that underlying truth will harmonize divergent faiths. True monism may well make room for what we call the machine, the mind, and the spirit of man and God.

Meanwhile we must all live private lives, laymen and scientists alike. We must run our course before an answer can come from science, and every thinking man must adopt for himself a faith to live by. He may take the best from man's ancient faiths. He must make the assumptions he considers reasonable as to the creation of the world and of mankind.

Last summer in London, at the three hundredth anniversary of the founding of the Royal Society, the oldest scientific body in the world, President Sir Cyril Hinshelwood made this statement: "The men of science themselves, as far as can be judged, have numbered about the same proportion of religious believers as the generality of people. Nor have they been conspicuously less well endowed with kindness or morality."

In attempting to describe a physiological basis of the mind here in San Francisco before this great symposium devoted to a study of the control of the mind, my predicament is like that of a certain astronomer who was invited to inaugurate the proceedings of a religious gathering by describing God's handiwork in outer space. There is a relationship. But it is difficult to define!

I have attempted to analyse the microcosm of forces and structures in the human brain. It is just as much God's handiwork as the stars and planets that move in outer space and just as vast in its complication. It should inspire in us no less awe than the macrocosm we call the firmament.

There is within us, each of us, the greatest wonder of all, the human brain. It holds a mirror up to the mind of man so man may see the stars and look into the future. With its help he may turn, as here and now in San Francisco, to examine the civilization he has himself created. And finally, using the brain to study the brain, man may succeed in the discovery of the nature of his own mind, and perhaps the purposes of God.

The University on the Burn-Side

A great university, with its halls and lawns and lofty elms, now stands on the slopes of Mount Royal. More than a century and a half ago when James McGill walked over these slopes, he found no life in the forest, only silence, and porcupines and beavers working in the burn. But the university was even then emerging in his mind, a place where the wisdom of the past would be taught, and where new knowledge and inspiration would appear, creating a lusty Canadian culture in the New World.

Today, it is not so much the academic halls and lawns that have realized his dream. It is the ideas and ideals of students, teachers and scholars. In a larger sense, it is the University's friends in Montreal and all who support it and know its fame and tell its story – they make it what it is and are a part of it. They all belong. And graduates enlarge it and carry it with them across the land and the sea. It is men who make a university.

McGill has always been an independent institution, a private university in the sense that Harvard and Yale and Princeton are private, and Bishop's in Quebec; and as Oxford and Cambridge are, or were before a British Welfare State began to introduce a new order of things. This university was built on the burn-side by the English-speaking pioneers of Montreal, without the help of church or state. It passed through perils and strange adventures. Peril and momentous decisions lie before it.

CONVOCATION ADDRESS, MCGILL UNIVERSITY, MONTREAL;
OCTOBER 1959.

Shortly after the year 1800, Lower Canada had its French-speaking ecclesiastical seminaries but there was no incorporated university north of the American border and no medical school. Montreal's population, only ten thousand, was largely French. But immigration from England and Scotland came with a rush about that time. James McGill died in 1813 leaving his woodland, and the fortune he had made in the fur trade, to found a university. It took shape first as a medical college.

The hospital accommodation of Montreal had been taxed to the limit by the arrival of so many English-speaking settlers. The Hôtel-Dieu, which had been founded in 1644 by a French gentlewoman, Jeanne Mance, to care for the sick of the city, was filled beyond capacity and the Sisters of St. Joseph were doing their best as they always have, and always will, no doubt.

But there was urgent need for something more. To meet the emergency, English-speaking women came to the rescue, forming the Female Benevolent Society of Montreal. They opened a four-bed hospital and gave it the optimistic title of "House of Recovery." That was in 1818. The following year, a group of local business men came to the rescue, taking over the hospital. They enlarged it and moved it, and so in 1822 the Montreal General Hospital opened its doors.

And here is where the story of a university begins. On the Medical Board of the new hospital there were four physicians all educated at Edinburgh University, which was then pre-eminent among the medical centres of Europe. Two of these men, Robertson and Caldwell, had been born in Scotland and came to Canada as army surgeons. The two younger physicians, Stephenson and Holmes, had been born here. In retrospect they seem to have been the real creators of our Medical School. After graduation from Edinburgh, they travelled together through the hospital and university centres of Europe and returned to Montreal with high hopes and great ambitions.

When the organizers of the new Montreal General Hospital made application for a charter, there was opposition in the legislature. A politician named O'Sullivan said, among other things, that if the charter were granted the patients in the new hospital would be experimented upon by the Edinburgh physicians! One of them, the former army surgeon, William

Caldwell, wrote an angry denial to the local newspaper, the *Courant*. He received, in return, a challenge to mortal combat from O'Sullivan. This was not child's play. The duel which followed was fought with pistols at close range. O'Sullivan received a bullet through his chest and Caldwell a shattered arm. Fortunately, both duellists recovered.

Following this dramatic prelude, the hospital charter was granted, and the doctors began to teach there and in a school, called the Montreal Medical Institution, at 20 St. James Street. They taught the whole body of medicine to keen young applicants. Shortly, they applied for permission to create what they called a "Seminary of Medical Learning." But incorporation was refused.

Two reasons were given for the refusal: first, they were not associated with an institution of learning, and, second, they had no endowment. That was in 1822. Unexpected help was at hand from another quarter. McGill University had been incorporated in 1821. But the organizers had only the land and the forest on the slopes of Mount Royal, far from the outskirts of the city. The money that James McGill had intended for support had yet to be won by litigation from the claims of other heirs. There were no students, no professors, and there had been no teaching yet. Delays ensued which only university administrators can understand! But eventually (1829), a meeting was called at Burnside Manor, the home that James McGill had built. The four doctors came to the meeting and were immediately declared Professors in the Faculty of Medicine of McGill University.

That first Faculty went into action the very day of the meeting. They continued to teach (as they had been doing for ten years), still without remuneration, at the Medical College on St. James Street and in the Montreal General Hospital nearby. But now, the newly-created professors were in charge of the only recognized medical college in Canada. They took in other teachers and, astonishing as it may seem, they established at once a four-year course in medicine although no college in the United States required more than two years at that time. They used the Edinburgh method of instruction at the bedside. This method of bedside teaching, modified and elaborated in Montreal, was to be introduced in the United States when McGill's William Osler became professor at Johns Hopkins more than a half century later. It was not until forty-three years after the meeting at Burnside Manor that the university opened a building for medicine on its own property. That was in 1872, the year young Osler graduated in medicine.

Of the founding physicians, Holmes proved to be the outstanding genius. His collection of herbs and flowers and minerals is still on view in the Redpath Museum. Students still strive to win the Holmes Gold Medal. His mantle has been worn with honour by his successors, Howard and Osler and Shepherd and Meakins and Archibald, as John Buchan's magic ring of genius* found its way into the hands of great men in succeeding generations.

Before Medicine was invited to its new home in the college grounds, a great deal had come to pass. No institution is worthy of the name of university unless the humanities are central in its organization. James McGill had planned a place where young Canadians might drink deep from the well of all learning, drink the waters that he had only tasted. He had not finished his classical studies at Glasgow University when he sailed away to Montreal. In time, he bought the wooded slopes of Mount Royal, high above the town. There, he must have fancied how academic buildings would rise on that height, and how students would look down on the city at the water's edge. He must have recalled how he had looked down on Glasgow thus, from the halls that top its University Hill, this man who was so much more than a dreamer.

After many delays, his fortune from the fur trade built a college of arts. But the college soon came on evil days in a cold and friendless world. No government supplemented its meagre income, as the founder had hoped it would. No church nor kindly educational group came to offer bounty. Through the long winter the professors heated the classrooms as best they could, burning maple wood from the forest. A handful of stu-

---

* John Buchan, *The Path of the King*. London: Hodder and Stoughton, 1921.

dents shivered with them about the fire, while bill-collectors came through the snow to hammer on the portal.

At last an editorial in the *Montreal Sun* warned that unless something was done quickly "McGill College will soon be numbered among the things that were."

Then – it was 1855 – a scholar and educator came to Montreal as the new Principal of McGill. The man was William Dawson, born in Pictou County, Nova Scotia. He, too, had been educated in Edinburgh University, as a geologist. But for five years before coming to Montreal he served as Superintendent of Education in Nova Scotia. In addition to his scientific distinction, which was shortly to be recognized by election to Fellowship in the Royal Society of London, young Dawson was a wise and kindly man with a quiet capacity for organization.

He made public a statement of the situation. He petitioned the Canadian Government for endowment. The Government's answer came back "no." But an answer came back "yes" from a new quarter – "yes" in swelling tones from the citizens of his own city. That, Sir William Dawson said forty years later, was "the beginning of a stream of liberality which has floated our University barque . . ."

Strong men, who had not yet been introduced to the income tax, gathered about Dawson. An academic heart began to beat in one faculty after another. These friends – the Molsons, Redpath, Strathcona, Workman, Macdonald and others – understood that Dawson must have support and freedom to act. They gave their fortunes to that end. And so it was that a great university was born beneath the trees of the forest where James McGill discovered only porcupines and silence and beavers working in the burn.

After thirty-eight years, when Principal Dawson retired, there were more than a thousand students and teachers on the college grounds. He rejoiced, for the University had taken a place of leadership. And the people of Montreal rejoiced, for the University had become part of the city, and the English-speaking citizens felt themselves part of the University, as they do today.

This is Founder's Day, the two hundred and sixteenth birthday of the pioneer fur-trader. His house, Burnside Manor, has disappeared, and even the woods and the burn are gone. City traffic echoes from the walls along Burnside Street.

But it is men who make a university. The dream of James McGill has come to life. The spirit of the founding physicians has never been lost, nor the inspiration of Sir William Dawson. There is no time for me to tell how the College grew, and how Rutherford began his epoch-making research on the nuclear structure of the atom there, sixty years ago. We cannot stop to laugh with Leacock, nor to mourn the death of the physician-poet, John McCrae, in Flanders Fields. We must not boast of our scholars and authors and scientists of today, nor tell the modern story of what McGill is doing for the nation.

The independent universities served society when there was no other place for higher learning and intellectual leadership. There is a particular role for them to play today—and tomorrow. Their friends today are no less keen to support them and keep them independent than they were a hundred years ago. But the stream of private liberality that floated Dawson's "university barque" flows less strongly now. Times have changed. The taxation pattern is drying it up.

A great university should have independent income. That means great endowments, along with annual grants, sufficient to make the members free to seek the truth and to speak it. Let our universities be supported, not directed. Let them be floated and left to chart their course toward greater knowledge and the ways of wisdom.

In closing, I would like to greet those who are here to celebrate with us the twenty-fifth birthday of the Montreal Neurological Institute. More than a hundred of you have returned in answer to our call—friends, former pupils, fellow-workers—to mark the close of the first quarter-century of service to mankind by this University Institute.

Some of you have had to come quite around the world, leaving your patients, your teaching and research. Affection, I know, and dedication to our common cause have brought you back to us. In the quest for understanding of the brain and mind of man, each explorer gains more distant vistas. You are one with us in a common endeavour, and we welcome you home to McGill.

Tennyson's well-remembered words which Ulysses spoke, returning from "the ringing plains of windy Troy," might well be your words:

> *I am a part of all that I have met;*
> *Yet all experience is an arch wherethro'*
> *Gleams that untravell'd world, whose margin fades*
> *For ever and for ever when I move.*

Neurosurgery —
Yesterday, Today and Tomorrow

[SIXTEEN]

Professor Edward Archibald was the first to practise the specialty of Neurosurgery in Canada. Since this distinguished surgeon and charming man is no longer here to welcome you, let him at least speak as he spoke to us in the opening ceremonies for the Montreal Neurological Institute.

"The nervous system is one of the most difficult parts of man's frame to understand. Few subjects in Medicine have demanded of investigators as great an intellectual capacity or as arduous a labour. And in that very fact lies the reason and the justification for neurological specialism. The earnest man knows that neurology demands his whole life. But his guerdon is great."

Yesterday, between 1870 and 1900, neurosurgery was born in England. Principles such as localization of function within the nervous system, asepsis, anaesthesia, were combined so as to make possible a new therapy. This was the period of advance in the basic science of our specialty.

Today, from 1900 to now, we see the evolution of the technique of the surgery of the nervous system, chiefly in the United States. It is a familiar pattern: basic science in Europe, applied science here; basic atomic research in Europe, the "atom bomb" here. I hope to indicate that the time has come for us to turn our attention to basic research as well as to its application.

Young surgeons who have learned to use the scalpel so

DINNER ADDRESS TO THE AMERICAN ACADEMY OF NEURO-SURGERY, IN MONTREAL; SEPTEMBER 1948.

expertly that they can take anything out of anywhere without a fatality, and who are able to cut the pathways of the currents of the intellect and leave a man who is still capable of walking, may be tempted to look upon the performance of the pioneers in the earlier period with unjustified contempt.

Elaboration of surgical techniques is an important mechanical achievement. But beware of vainglory; for it may be that our intellectual maturity is yet far off, and to be acquired only after years of further pioneering.

While Edward Jenner, a country practitioner, was elaborating the hypothesis that he hoped would control the world's worst plague, namely smallpox, John Hunter wrote to him, "Don't think, try; be patient, be accurate." Twenty years later Jenner tried, with the result that a million lives were saved.

Today we seem to be in so great a hurry! Often we listen only to the first part of Hunter's injunction: "Don't think, try."

Tomorrow? What of Tomorrow? I believe that a new day will dawn tomorrow and that in its light will be found an understanding of the nervous system. Mental as well as physical activity will then be recognized as a function of the brain, and neurosurgery and psychiatry will gradually lose the separate authority conferred upon them by ignorance until there remains only neurology. Neurology will then stand forth as a single discipline to which internist, psychologist, surgeon, chemist and physiologist will contribute.

But before the dawn of that new day, applied science must wait for the development of basic science. The neurosurgeon stands now in a strategic position. He alone can solve certain problems in human physiology, but he must stop to heed John Hunter's words, "be patient, be accurate." He must perceive the basic problems which block our advance, must think physiologically, chemically, anatomically or pathologically. The type of early training he has received will probably determine the manner of his thinking, if he thinks at all. Each can approach some problem according to his own ability, his own training, and according to the cry that reaches his ears from suffering humanity.

Perhaps, after all, we need a longer perspective when considering neurological surgery. More than two thousand years before Christ the Egyptians had innumerable specialists. As Herodotus expressed it, some undertook "to cure diseases of the eye, the others of the head, others again of the teeth, others of the intestines, and some those which are not local."

For two millenniums these specialists continued to practise and to collect fees without making the slightest advance. Indeed, they steadily degenerated. The trouble was that the Egyptians made a fatal mistake. They wrote textbooks, the hermetic books. They made another and more serious mistake, and that was to believe that the textbooks were correct. So they forbade physicians, at peril of their lives, to depart in any way from the treatment prescribed in the hermetic books. It was a remarkable experiment. Science, and art, and religion and education as well, were frozen by rules which, when originally written, may well have been the best that could be drawn up. The experiment demonstrated that standardization can halt advance but that it does not in any way hinder retrogression.

There was, however, one thing we inherited directly from the Egyptians and that was the charm, the incantation, which every physician invokes today to banish evil from the drugs he uses. I refer to the R with crossed tail which mysteriously heads all of our prescriptions. This is the eye of Horus, who was the Egyptian god of health.

Few physicians, and reputedly no surgeons, know what they are doing when they write a prescription today! Perhaps the knowledge that they have called upon such an ancient and honourable deity to free their formulas of any curse should be a consolation to them. In any case, I like to think that somewhere, in a forgotten Egyptian heaven, Horus is chuckling about it. On the other hand, it may well be that he looks down upon this new generation of specialists with alarm, lest they too should come to worship the perfection of their own achievement. When you standardize treatment and training, beware that basic science is not again frozen, as it was in ancient Egypt.

Neurosurgery is an exacting mistress. She demands much time and effort from the specialists who would follow her. I propose to inquire into her past and her derivation. The exact date of her birth is uncertain.

The great Joseph Lister once operated upon a patient for a

brain tumour which had been localized for him by David Ferrier. When the dura was opened the pressure was so alarming that the operator plunged his thumb into the protruding cortex. Clear fluid gushed forth, as though he had used the rod of Aaron. Autopsy, which was not long delayed, showed that he had missed the tumour by a fraction of an inch. That, however, was not the beginning of neurosurgery. Nor would it have been if the luckless patient had happened to be relieved of his trouble, for many of the basic principles on which the specialty had to be built were still unrecognized.

In 1884 Rickman Godlee, a nephew of Lister, removed a brain tumour in the operating room of the Hospital for the Paralysed and Epileptic in Queen Square. The localization had been made for him by Hughes Bennett, according to the theory of cerebral localization lately enunciated by Broca, Fritsch, Hitzig, Ferrier and Jackson.

But, again, this performance was not the beginning of neurosurgery. The localization was accurate, the surgery faulty. The brave young Scot who laid himself upon the operating table that day died weeks later of an operative infection. But the event may be looked upon as the prologue to neurosurgery, the curtain-raiser.

Wilfred Trotter, referring to this operation fifty years later, said,

> We shall not get a proportioned view of our event unless we pause a moment to call up the world in which it took place. In 1884 we find ourselves in the richest depths of the Victorian era, and the warm tranquil air of its impenetrable security closes round us. . . . The land belonged to its monarchs, the seas belonged to England, and the firmament was unconquered though perhaps still a little vaguely claimed by the Church. In science the air was yet unadulterated with inert gases, and matter still sat contentedly in its little hard globular and indestructible atoms.

There was a neurosurgeon who could write as well as operate! Those who were to play the leading role in the birth of our specialty followed every detail of this operation. Sir David

Ferrier and Hughlings Jackson stood anxiously in mask and white coat to see the tumour come out, and two young surgeons, Victor Horsley and William Macewen, were in the audience when the case was reported.

I suspect that the first formulation of essential principles of neurological surgery took place in the minds of these two young men during the extended discussion of Godlee's case. I can imagine them listening to the enthusiastic talk of Ferrier, for only the year before, in his Marshall Hall oration, he had concluded his discussion of experimental brain operations in mammals with the argument that the time had come for the beginning of neurological surgery. I am sure the young men would have sought out Hughlings Jackson, then fifty years of age. Jackson had delivered a series of lectures eleven years before on "The Diagnosis of Tumours of the Brain" and two years before on "Localized Convulsions from Tumour of the Brain." No doubt, also, there was much conversation with the indefatigable clinician, William Gowers, then thirty-nine years of age.

At all events, Horsley, who had just begun a brilliant series of physiological experiments of his own, found time to report a series of ten human craniotomies in 1886, and two years later he reported with William Gowers the first successful removal of an accurately localized tumour from the spinal canal. In the same year Macewen reported twenty-one craniotomies for brain abscess with eighteen astonishing recoveries. Perhaps the secret of this success lies in his first case which was not included in the twenty-one. I fancy that it was on his return to Glasgow from the discussion of Godlee's operation in London that he diagnosed an abscess in the frontal lobe of a boy. The parents refused permission for operation, but he secured the autopsy, tapped the abscess and inserted the drain, thus rehearsing step by step the procedure which was to save many lives. From basic science he had advanced to applied science.

Neurosurgery had had its birth, but not yet its baptism. It was not named a specialty and the technique those surgeons used was so crude as to bring a blush of shame today to the cheek of any member of this Academy.

I have begun with discussion of neurology and neurological

surgery in London and have referred to the evolution of certain basic principles which were indispensable to the beginning of our specialty. For the next stage in its development we must turn to the United States, where a group of surgeons elaborated the technique, thereby reducing mortality to a reasonable level.

Harvey Cushing, surgical resident at Johns Hopkins, went abroad in 1900. Horsley had become too busy with practice and politics to be interested in his training. In Berne he worked on a neurophysiological problem suggested to him by Kocher, drifted back to Liverpool to watch Sherrington experimenting with anthropoids, and on returning to Baltimore asked Professor Halsted if he might specialize in the surgery of the nervous system. Halsted suggested that he might better take up something useful, like orthopaedics!

However, in 1913, when he left Baltimore for Boston, he had become a specialist, a neurosurgeon; and in 1920 the Society of Neurological Surgeons was founded. In the next quarter of a century the specialty came of age under the leadership of Cushing, Dandy, Frazier, Sachs, Mixter and others. This was the period of technical evolution.

Not all leaders in neurosurgery were primarily surgeons. Otfrid Foerster, of Breslau, was a neurologist who assisted Kutner, the Professor of Surgery, for a time until abruptly, in an upsurge of impatience, he seized the scalpel himself. As might be expected, his contributions lay in the field of neurological mechanisms, not surgical technique. Neurosurgery for him was an opportunity to study pathological physiology and anatomy. Clovis Vincent, likewise, was a neurologist who slipped directly into neurosurgery after assisting Dr. de Martel.

Tomorrow in neurosurgery depends on the planning of today. It is splendid for men to be trained in surgery and apprenticed to neurosurgeons until they can carry out every standard procedure. That may be the "strait gate" and the "narrow way" of the orthodox. But there are other ways of entering the "kingdom of Heaven." I am sure that the great god Horus would join me in a plea that certificating boards should not close the gate to those who choose another approach. Not everyone can have a perfectly balanced training. Leave a crack in the gate wide enough to admit those of us who have had only surgical experience without approved neurosurgical apprenticeship, and for those with apprenticeship but with little general surgery.

The fields in which advance will be made "are white already to harvest." Those capable of taking in that harvest are few indeed. If there must be standardizing tests, and I suppose there must be, let them be intellectual ones and leave loopholes in the rules of time of service. Remember that the Egyptians achieved remarkable things in medicine and then retrogressed through two millenniums of standardized specialization.

My advice to men entering the field is to learn to speculate reasonably regarding cause and effect. When it is that you learn this, what time you spend at it, and how you achieve it matters very little. It is never too late. Close up the flower of your busy practice for a few months. It may be then that your surgical tree will bear good fruit, whatever its past history.

Some men think in anatomical terms, others neurologically, psychologically, pathologically, physiologically, even chemically. There should be no room in our cult for those who think only financially, socially or not at all. Let certification boards aim to keep these men out, if indeed there are any such seeking admission.

It is enough for us to learn to think about our problems in terms of a basic science and learn to operate with adequate safety. This brings great spiritual reward (to which, fortunately, financial reward is usually added!). To use the quaint phraseology of Archibald, the "guerdon is great"; and then he added: "To gather knowledge and to find out new knowledge is the noblest occupation of the physician. To apply that knowledge . . . with sympathy born of understanding, to the relief of human suffering, is his loveliest occupation."

It is a source of satisfaction, no doubt, to devise technical procedures and to invent new gadgets. But this, it seems to me, is nothing compared with the reward that comes to a man when he at length evolves a general principle from many isolated observations.

Such a deduction may come to him suddenly, like a flash, while he is talking. It may come late at night when he is alone, writing out his analysis of observations. It may come when he has turned his mind quite away from the problem. But when it comes it is the result of his own intellectual effort. Whenever scientific creation comes to a man, and however unimportant it may seem to others, it is for him an exciting experience that he will not forget in his lifetime. The task of testing and retesting his principle is not a task at all for him, for each time he finds verification of his thesis there will return to him something of the exaltation of that first excitement.

Finally, what constitutes the specialty of Neurosurgery? A body of accepted basic principles, yes, and a group of technical and operative procedures which conform to these principles. But something more—the alluring promise of new discovery. I have already pointed out that this is what makes her such an irresistible mistress. It is the call which explorers feel, I suppose; difficult to explain but powerful. Kipling called it an "everlasting whisper." "Something hidden. Go and find it. Go and look behind the ranges—something lost behind the ranges. Lost and waiting for you. Go!"

The promise of discovery may be found in other special fields as well as in the nervous system, but nowhere is the future so full of promise, the possibility of advance so unlimited, and the results of research so important to mankind.

A Doctor's Philosophy

SEVENTEEN

An hour ago, the talk and laughter of students in the spring
sunshine sounded across the lawns and echoed back triumph-
antly from the walls of this university, your Alma Mater. Now,
in the silence of Convocation, you who were students this morning wait for your diplomas, wait to kneel before the Vice-
Chancellor and stand up, Doctors of Medicine.

This is a time set aside for introspection and for dreaming
the dreams of the future. Indeed, the chief virtue of the convocation address, which I have the honour to deliver to you, is
that it provides the graduands with a period of enforced reverie,
at last.

Each man may look to his own horizons, forward and back, to
right and left. You know by now that it takes a great deal more
than medical science to make a good doctor. You have competed
for the highest honours in the classroom, and on the playing
field. But you leave this competition behind you, along with
the pleasant ways of college life.

Looking to the vistas that lie before, I shall talk of things
that find no place in textbooks – of medical heroes, a personal
plan for education, a doctor's philosophy, of death, and that
strange psychological bond between Doctor and Patient, and
finally of family life. First, a short detour, and then I shall
return to these things, one by one, and you will follow me still,
I hope.

Speaking to you as I do today, I am like a shepherd in the
Middle East, in Mesopotamia. He does not drive his sheep as

ADDRESS AT THE MEDICAL CONVOCATION, QUEEN'S
UNIVERSITY, KINGSTON, ONTARIO; MAY 1957.

a shepherd would in the West. He walks before them calling aloud, and they "baa" back in differing keys, but they follow. The peculiar thing about his call, as I have listened to it, is that it resembles the voice of a sheep so closely in tone and timing. Thus, sheep and shepherd pass through the town and over the hillside, seeming to speak one language.

In years to come you will recall my voice as you heard it today, but not my words. You'll remember your thinking but not my thoughts. I know the paths that you must follow, for I have been what you will be: student, practitioner, teacher, explorer.

The Lebanese poet, Kahlil Gibran, has described the limitations of a lecturer. "No man," he wrote, "can reveal to you aught but that which already lies asleep in the dawning of your knowledge. . . . For the vision of one man lends not its wings to another man."

*　　*　　*

You have your own personal heroes, no doubt. All men need them. They constitute a private possession, shut away from the world, in a hidden chamber of the mind. Your heroes go about with you. They are your good spirits. At times, they seem to stand at the door of your conscience. They may warn but they never command.

Most Canadian physicians would, I suppose, admit that Osler is one of their heroes. He is one of mine. Because he may be one of yours, I shall pause to describe him. I knew him when I was a medical student, and lived in his home in Oxford in April, 1916, convalescing from a broken leg. One well-remembered evening, I sat with Lady Osler and their only son, Revere, while Sir William read aloud his final draft of an address called "Creators, Transmuters and Transmitters: Shakespeare, Bacon and Burton". He had prepared it for the opening of a Shakespeare exhibit that was to be held in the Bodleian Library, next day.

I can see him now at his desk in his study. The study door that during the day had opened so pleasantly on the garden was closed now, and shadows fell on his precious books that lined the walls. In the desk-lamp's soft reflection, I could see the face of

William Harvey looking down from the frame above the mantel. He seemed to be listening too, with approval.

The reader was a slender man with high forehead, dark skin, drooping moustaches. He showed a keen interest in form and meaning. He was concerned with the quality of workmanship, like a cabinet-maker who runs his finger over smooth surface and secret joint, reconsidering the work of his hands.

When he had finished, I remember Lady Osler's quiet questions, her final words of approval. I knew how much he relied on her criticism and how close they had grown in understanding over the years. Revere made suggestions too, and I can see Sir William's answering smile.

It may encourage you, as it does me, to realize that, in his early days, this master craftsman was neither a good writer nor a good speaker. You have only to read his earliest addresses to be convinced of that. Hard work and a faithful system of short periods for reading converted him into an admirable scholar and a polished writer. In the same way, too, he became a great pathologist and clinician by virtue of hard, systematic work.

Nevertheless, it was not so much the quality of his intellect that made him, in his day, an almost universal hero of Medicine, and a source of Canadian pride like Sir Frederick Banting. The quality that was unique in Osler had to do with the heart. It was his kindness, compassion, humour, understanding.

The Greek philosopher, Socrates, admitted that he had a personal deity, a private genius, that spoke to him at times. He called it his "daimon" and he listened when it spoke to his inner self. But when he was being tried for his life, he listened in vain, for the daimon was silent. And so when the judgement went against him, he drank the deadly hemlock, spurning the chance to escape.

Each of you has chosen his heroes. Get to know them as well as you can. You will add others as the years pass, and they will speak to you of secret aims and dreams. They will help you to shape and to re-shape your ambitions. But if you expect them to make decisions for you, you will be disappointed, like Socrates with his daimon.

*   *   *

No doctor, even though he holds a diploma in his hands, should think of himself as more than a student. He is committed to a life of continuing, self-regulated, post-graduate education, first because of the enormous complexity of the field of medicine, secondly because of the breathless pace of modern advance in medical research and thirdly because every physician expects to have his own personal projects of exploration.

Allow me a sidelong glance at university education. The initial training of physicians is, all too often it seems to me, deficient on the side of the Humanities. It is not enough for universities to train the medical student in basic science and in technique. He must be more than a technician. He should read foreign languages. He should be able to express himself in good English. He should read it and write it. He should learn to enjoy some aspect of Literature, have some hobby in the Arts. These are not undue requirements for a man who is to be spiritual counsellor to educated men and women as well as the keeper of their bodies.

Universities that, by their curricular organization, do not encourage doctors to make a good beginning in the Humanities before their immersion in the waters of Biology, allow them to emerge into the practice of medicine with a cultural handicap.

The sky that arches above the field of medicine is higher than men think and its horizons more distant. Edna St. Vincent Millay's words come to me:

> *. . . brewed*
> *From stronger meat must be the broth we give.*
> *Blue, bright September day, with here and there*
> *On the green hills a maple turning red*
> *And white clouds racing in the windy air! —*
> *If I would help, I must be fed*
> *In wit and purpose, pour away despair.*

Universities, at best, can do little more than lead men to the threshold of their understanding, teach them how to educate themselves. Thus you must now consider Literature and Language along with Medicine in your present plans. Culture is an expression of the way of life. If Osler became a scholar as the result of well-organized reading after his initial training, others can do the same. Travel and discussion and interest in the affairs of men contribute much. But most important is the planned "way of life."

But that plan must apply to two people, not one, since most doctors marry, early or late. It may seem incredible to an unprejudiced observer; but there are women, even those in their right mind, who are willing to marry physicians – and the loveliest women at that! This event is usually the most important and critical one in a doctor's whole career.

A convocation speaker can do no more than contemplate this phenomenon. I see before me now the wives of nearly half of these newly made Doctors, and other young women who might seem to be drifting dangerously in that direction. What I am about to say is for them too.

The entrance of a wife into a doctor's life is what an insurance broker might call "an act of God." Inevitably, she takes into her charming hand the balance for him, between success and failure – the balance for them both, between happiness and despair.

In addition to his working-place in office or hospital or laboratory, a doctor should have a desk of his own at home in a study where he keeps his books and personal files.

There has never been a time in my life when I did not bring home material to study at night. On arrival I might find a toy on my desk to be mended, left by a youngster who was sure that "Daddy could fix it." After dinner the family might crowd into the study for coffee and an hour of talk or reading. Even a doctor must laugh and relax. He must be a husband and a father to a growing family if he is lucky enough to have one. It is good to read aloud for a little time. A man who wants a contented wife and grateful children must set aside an evening or two for weekly entertainment, must plan companionship in vacation time. But a man's study has a door that can be shut on occasion.

I have not talked of annual trips to clinics and hospitals. It is obvious that no practitioner can serve his patients well today without taking "refresher courses." The specialist must get away from his practice for months at a time. I took my family with me on three such journeys abroad and once I had to borrow money to do it.

While you are writing a medical paper or report you can learn simplicity and clarity of expression by regular readings from Shakespeare, the King James version of the Bible, Shaw or many of the poets. At one period in my life my favourite bedside author was Edna St. Vincent Millay, whose sonnet I have quoted.

But every man has his own preference. I must confess that I could never bring myself to care for Osler's preferred selections, such as Thomas Browne's *Religio Medici*. You will probably not be able to stomach the literary food that suits my palate. But if you want to express yourself clearly and write well you must read well, even if it can only be in brief snatches.

The pattern of a doctor's day and the number of hours of his sleep depend on the rhythm of his metabolism, no doubt. You cannot change these things. You may work best at your desk before breakfast, as I do. Or, you may work best late at night. There is no place for alcohol in work routine.

So much for what you might call the doctor's extracurricular post-graduate training. Now a word in regard to his medical curriculum after college.

"Cramming" as a method of mastering the subject at the close of a college course is a very poor substitute for a year of daily study. But as a supplement to previous hard work, you have doubtless discovered that it serves its useful purpose in the examination hall. In later life the ability to "cram" is a most important asset. The clinician is able thus to review all that is known about a subject and to hold it in mind, at least until the emergency is past.

To do this he must have reference books and his own summary notes. He must have a system. My system is to use cards that fit in my pocket and later into an index box. On these cards go the summaries of what I read, notes of lectures heard, account of hospitals visited, operations seen, drawings of other men's procedures and their instruments and laboratory techniques. This is very useful during the hospital service period. In later life it is indispensable while at medical meetings and on medical travels.

There is a psychology of the doctor-patient relationship which some physicians never seem to comprehend. It is the patient's instinctive desire to clothe his or her doctor in a mantle of authority. It serves the patient as a reassurance when he is insecure and frightened. An honest doctor may blush to wear it, but a wise one does not protest.

Let me give you one specific piece of advice – just one. Don't express premature judgments that you may have to retract. Keep your mouth shut about what you think, in the outset. Get the patient's history completely. Be stern while you stop his unrelated chatter. Examine him. If it is a child, learn the mother's opinion and, still more important, the grandmother's. Collect the evidence. Finally give your opinion and treatment and prognosis, expressed with honest frankness. You may wear the mantle of Hippocrates then with comfort and, who knows, you may even deserve it.

*　　*　　*

Men rarely mention death. They shun the very thought of it. But death, untimely death, is the physician's time-honoured adversary. We struggle with him each time he approaches the door of the sick-room. We wrestle against him, as Hercules did when he brought Alcestis back, "up from the world of darkness," and returned her to her husband. But in the end, inevitably, there comes a day when death will win. It is then our task to usher him in. Moreover, we know, full well, that there are sick-rooms where death is welcome. He enters as the patient's best friend, the patient who is hopeless and longing to go.

There has been recent public criticism of our profession, that we sometimes hold death off too long. This is partly justified. I have seen death postponed for the head of a family who suffers on, while the money he had saved in better days, for the future of wife and child, vanishes. Our critics might bear in mind, however, that the trouble is not in science but in the uses men make of it. Doctor and layman alike must learn wisdom in their employment of science, whether this applies to atom bomb or blood transfusion.

There are times when compassion should prompt us to forgo prolonged and costly treatment. If a man must die, he has the right to die in peace, as he would prefer to do if asked. Positive action to take a life is not permitted. But the negative decisions that ease and shorten suffering have always been ours to make. Perhaps the public is ignorant of the fact that good physicians do such things silently, not publishing abroad what they are about. Their guide to action may be found in the Master's words: "All things whatsoever ye would that men should do to you, do ye even so to them; for this is the law and the prophets."

* * *

It is the urgent need that physicians should know themselves, should define their own beliefs. They should establish their own philosophy since they must deal with death and life, with hope and black despair, and with human frailty. When you entered medical school some of you may have found your childhood faiths too simple. You saw man, made "in the image of God," lying outstretched in the dissecting room. You studied life's mechanisms in many forms while no mention was made of the spirit. And so you may have felt, as I did, that in the light of new knowledge and new experience, it was necessary to re-argue your philosophy.

In the past decade I have been preoccupied with the physiology of the human brain. How is it that nerve impulses, travelling through the brain, are translated into thought? And, turning the problem about, how can thinking express itself in nerve conduction? What, and where, are the mechanisms that must function when a man is conscious, the mechanisms that are stilled when he is unconscious?

One thing is clear from all this study: Science cannot yet explain the mind in terms of brain mechanisms. Perhaps it may never be able to do so. Intelligent men who contemplate the mind and the spirit of Man, men who ponder the conception of God and the question of life after death, should realize that science cannot help them in their thinking. Reasonable men must therefore adopt what seem to them to be reasonable beliefs in regard to the ultimate nature of the universe.

The Hindu philosopher, S. Radhakrishnan, said in his Beatty

Lectures,* "The human mind is sadly crippled in its religious thinking by the belief that the truth has been found, embodied, standardized" once and for all.

"My philosophy," Louis Pasteur, the great French biologist, wrote to a friend, "is of the heart and not of the mind. I give myself up . . . to those feelings about eternity which come naturally at the bedside of a cherished child drawing its last breath."

For my own part, such instinctive thinking as that described by Pasteur is not enough. Reason should also enter into it. Belief in God should be a reasoned and reasonable act of faith. Each man must approach his God in his own way, using the form of worship that suits him best. Most men may find this in the church of their childhood, and it is not for the doctor, not even for the psychiatrist, to interfere.

But, aside from all this, your patients, facing the tragedy of death, or the tragedy of life, will turn to you over and over again for the immediate help that you can give.

"Think on these things." You are shepherds, not sheep. And over the hillsides of Medicine, the sky is blue, the horizons wide. The windy air will bring you thrilling challenge now and always, if you can do your work with wit and purpose.

---

* *East and West.* London: Allen and Unwin, 1955.

Mankind in the Atomic Age

"What can I say about Mankind in the Atomic Age? Is it enough to tell the thoughts that come to me in the face of the possible extinction of society?" That was what I heard myself saying over a cup of breakfast coffee, not long ago. My wife left the table and looked into the canary's cage. Then she went out to the kitchen for bird-seed.

"Yes," she said, "but it's not going to happen."

Well, that is one way of dealing with the atomic threat, to forget it and take care of the canary instead. My wife may be right – for some years. Political leaders sometimes use threats to serve a purpose, without intention of fulfilment. But we have entered the atomic age and threats will surely lead to action some day, unless man takes his destiny into his own hands at last. The loss of a life, even one's own life, is not so important. But the loss of the grandeur, the beauty, the good that man has created! That is something too dreadful to contemplate.

In some countries men cannot express their thoughts freely. We can. We can do so without danger of being banished or imprisoned. In this McGill Symposium no person, and no institution, is exempt from possible criticism. To one who returns from travel through the world, this is a wind of challenge. Wise criticism is so much needed and ears are so deaf to wisdom.

National leaders talk of armaments for defence in the current "cold war" between East and West. No mention is made of offence. It is clear enough that if the forces of atomic power were ever loosed, no one would win. There is only one way of

SYMPOSIUM DISCUSSION, MCGILL UNIVERSITY, OCTOBER 1961.

winning this cold war. That is by an offensive of human understanding and friendship waged by the people on one side
against the people on the other. If this campaign were to succeed, both sides would be the winners. I do not refer to nation-
alist propaganda, conducted by a governmental agency; I refer
to a national uprising of the people to create international
understanding. An uprising of people who have no desire to
proselyte and who are willing to discover that the philosophy
and social system and religion on the other side suit their needs
there, as ours suit us.

"Preposterous!" you may say. "People will not turn away from
self-seeking and entertainment long enough to learn a foreign
language and to visit foreign lands. Fantastic proposal!" But it
would seem neither preposterous nor fantastic to the survivor
of a bomb explosion within Canadian frontiers.

Leagues and world police and unions of nations would work
effectively even in the atomic age, but only if based on friendly
understanding, only if we and others make the effort to get
acquainted. Mr. Kennedy's Peace Corps is a small move in the
right direction. But I refer to nations, not to corps. This great
organized offensive campaign might well succeed, because it
would be based on the exploitation of the good that is present
deep in the hearts of all men. There may be bad there as well,
but goodness and kindness are always present. I know what I
am talking about in this regard. I am a doctor and I have looked
into the hearts and minds of men and women. I have come to
know physicians who have done the same, all around the world.

Look back with me for a moment. Man with his wonderful
brain has created an astonishing state of things on this ancient
planet. Life here in many forms is very old. It was developed,
if not created, by the vastly slow process of species-evolution.
But the evolution of a human society has been comparatively
brief – a few thousand years, no more. It really began, I suspect,
with the appearance of the present model of brain, the model
you and I carry around with us. As soon as it came into existence
in the head of *homo sapiens,* the evolution of this civilization
was inevitable. It could have been predicted with man's arts and
skills, his accumulating knowledge, and his science.

Man himself is responsible for this amazing evolution of

society and civilization. Mankind has created the present dilemma and mankind must find a way out, or another race may be destroyed. It has happened before. The purposes of destruction were just as bestial when Ur and Sumeria were blotted out. But the work was less efficiently done. Who knows? Perhaps this time the Eskimos and the New Zealanders, who might survive an all-out atomic war, would breed a wiser and a kindlier race of men! But that is a sorry cynicism, and this is neither the time nor the place for cynicism.

The vast majority of thinking men on this earth probably wish there were no such thing as an atom weapon. The dilemma could be cured, at least temporarily, by disarmament. But a more basic cure for the disease of war is called for.

It is idle to reproach the men of science because they gave the world the secrets of the atom. Such knowledge was inevitable in time. That scientific "break-through" was made in the West. It was the heads of the American and British governments who decided to use the bomb in the last war, and however much we may regret that decision now, we can only reflect that no one asked the opinion of the man in the street. No one would wait to ask our opinions now about such matters if, on some quiet night, the dreadful messenger of atom war should flash across the heavens.

We bear no ill will against the Russian and Chinese people, and we know that our government and the elected leaders of our American and British allies have no plans of unprovoked aggression against those countries. Nevertheless, their leaders say they have reason to fear it, and so our leaders fear them, and we fear. We can hardly help recalling that successive spokesmen for the Supreme Soviet have, in the not too distant past, pledged themselves to extend their philosophy and political organization to all nations. We remember that Adolf Hitler published his plan of conquest before 1939. Many could not believe that he was serious. But millions died to stop him.

We see that the U.S.S.R. is still holding the nations of central Europe in her control. Now, sixteen years after capture, these countries are still deprived of self-determination. Until they are free, I would never urge the United States to lessen the power of her military establishment unilaterally, or to abandon her policy of *containment*. We have supported this policy already. Unless we in Canada are willing to urge the U.S.A. to lay down all atomic weapons without similar action on the part of Soviet Russia, we should not talk of doing so ourselves.

I do not suggest that Canada should follow American foreign policies without stubborn consideration. The continuing freedom of this country is proof to all the world that our neighbour does not seek enlargement and has been a friend to us in time of peace and in recent wars. We should use that freedom for constructive criticism, as an ally, to help her find the path of wisdom in her dealings with all nations, and particularly with our other neighbour to the north of us, the U.S.S.R., and our gigantic neighbour to the west where millions are on the march, and centuries of seeming slumber are at an end.

What I propose is an offensive of understanding, brotherhood, friendship by the people of the West toward the people of the East. Those in the East have accepted our science and our mechanized culture. They would accept our friendship if it were activated. This is not visionary. It is the only way. Statesmanship is almost powerless today and war has changed its nature. That warrior and statesman, Winston Churchill, said in 1949 when the last world war was over: "The fulfilment of spiritual duty in our daily life is vital to our survival."

Somehow we must mobilize our spiritual strength. How can men in our selfish society be roused? Others must answer that question. If as much space in our publications were devoted to this cause as that now allotted to advertising alcoholic beverages, a start would be made. Brands of food and drink and clothes are not advertised in communist countries, but "propaganda" is.

Men, women and children, for their own salvation, must turn to this task with a new dedication and a new leadership. Here are some essential and practical steps in the campaign:

(1) Recognition of China by Canada and the United States, as already carried out in Great Britain;

(2) Establishment of Russian and Chinese courses of language instruction by native teachers in a few schools in every area, as well as in all the universities;

(3) Promotion of foreign travel by our people and their people, on every level of social organization . . . but not for the idle tourist in search of amusement. I refer especially to visitors in organized fields such as those of the University, Medicine, Law, Farming, Art, Business, Engineering, Trade, Religion, Sports.

These are my thoughts about mankind in the atomic age. Deep in the heart of every man, in every nation, there is a well of kindness. It holds the sovereign cure for war and strife, the only cure. What is wanted, I suppose, is a completely sincere *religion* of the *Brotherhood of Man*, acceptable to all men in and out of every party, church, and cult.

The Use of Idleness

[NINETEEN]

"Leisure and the Medical Student" was the topic Dean Sunderland assigned to me for this symposium. It started me to thinking, as wise assignments often do. Rather an absurd title, it seemed, as I looked back to my years in medical school. Ask almost any medical student and he will probably say he does not know what leisure is. Has age discovered something new?

A scholar in Ancient Greece must have been one who used his leisure to good advantage. The Greek word *skholê* meant leisure, and our words "school" and "scholar" come from that. But after all, in the twentieth century, leisure provides the only time a conscientious individual may allow himself for idleness. What about that? The dictionary gives "fruitlessness" as its synonym. Idleness may produce no evidence of immediate fruit, but it is not inactivity. That would be sleep or stupor in the case of a man. The motor of the automobile which is idling is turning over, purring smoothly without declared objective. For a man, idleness should properly be defined – what shall I say? – as activity without effort; delightfully fruitless activity like children's play. And here is a highly important paradox: children's play is the most creative and constructive nonsense in the whole field of education.

In Canada, the season of college convocations comes in June. Consequently, when I was called upon to speak, I selected "Idleness" for my topic. The press report came to the attention of our Dean of Medicine at McGill University and prompted him

ADDRESS AT THE SYMPOSIUM ON "SOME ASPECTS OF MEDICAL EDUCATION", UNIVERSITY OF MELBOURNE MEDICAL SCHOOL CENTENARY; AUGUST 1962.

to add his paradox to mine. He wrote some verses which he sent to me while I was preparing this talk. An academic chain-reaction had flashed around the world, from Dean to Dean.

The title of the poem was "A Plea for the Seeming Idle." Here is a part of it:

Pragmatic axles turn on emptiness

(A wonderful line, that! Dean Lloyd Stevenson tells me it is quoted from the writings of Taoism, the ancient Chinese religion founded by Lao-tsu a century before the time of Hippocrates. But the rest of the poem flows from the Dean's own pen.)

> *Pragmatic axles turn on emptiness*
> *And seraph wings in the blue air find purchase,*
> *Proving that nothing may have something in it*
> *At any flashing paradoxical minute*
> *And that we ought to wait upon its power*
> *Before we turn industriously sour*
> *And lose the vehemence of the phoenix hour.*

Deans, you see, have strange flashes of insight not granted, perhaps, to ordinary men. But let me turn back to the medical student; he could be right after all. If he continues to think only of medicine in his times off, he has no time off, and he has little rest. Real rest from the day's job is doing something else, doing something that brings you delightful preoccupation such as comes to a child in his play. A happy child passes from one project to another all day long, using mind and body as hard as he can, until he falls asleep suddenly, exhausted by a succession of fruitless tasks that he calls "fun."

The same is true in other walks of life. Men in a hurry believe that they can take no leisure. And so we live in a world of tiresome specializing experts who talk more and more of their own occupational *expertise*. I have changed the title of this talk, since what I wish to say goes far beyond the medical student.

The thesis that I shall undertake to prove calls for a fundamental change of approach to education. Every specialist, whatever his profession, skill or business may be, can improve his performance by broadening his base. It is a way of life I am talking about, not extra college courses.

Reading is one of the ways of doing this. Strange as it may seem, some professional men rarely read. They study, and they glance at the newspaper or listen to the radio while doing something else; but they rarely read. When I was laboriously writing out a description of my first serious contribution to medical science, my wife and I decided to try out an experiment. We read Shakespeare's *Hamlet* aloud, as often as we could, over the coffee in that all-too-brief interval that followed dinner, after the young ones were in bed. Hearing Shakespeare use the words of our language is sheer delight, and although science reporting is not poetry (far from it!), the echo of his rhythms, we thought, could do my writing little harm. To imitate almost anything is the challenge a child accepts in his play. And a man who will not let the windows of his mind be closed, continues to revive the child he keeps shut up in working hours.

Of course, if you do not happen to be a reader, you can marry one, with luck. If neither of you is given to reading, or if you live alone, try it out none the less, and you will like it. But take it regularly in small doses. I am little impressed by the man who devours whole books in a night. But this may be due to jealousy, for I am a slow and plodding reader.

Today, when there is so much a man could learn, any university student or any serious scholar may well ask: "How can I afford to take time from my major project in life and spend it on anything else? 'Life is so short and the Art so long.' "

The scholar who is honest with himself today can hardly avoid being discouraged at times when he considers how little remains in the mind of all that he hears and sees and studies, and how little he discovers for himself. Sir Isaac Newton confessed to such a feeling: "To myself," he said, "I seem to have been only like a boy playing on the sea-shore, and diverting myself in now and then finding a smoother pebble or a prettier shell than ordinary, whilst the great ocean of truth lay all undiscovered before me."

That was 250 years ago, after Newton had discovered the laws of gravity. Many facts have been added since then, and more theories. Today a student seems to stand on the shore beside a vast, restless sea, the sea of man's recorded knowledge, watching it alter with the changing winds of man's opinions. We, too, may pick up sea-shells and pebbles on the shore; but they seem so few and unimpressive!

The scholar can no longer encompass all knowledge like Aristotle, nor master all skills like Leonardo da Vinci. That time has passed long since. The scholar's problem today is to cover one area of knowledge. But he must know how to find out anything he needs to learn. That is what modern scholarship is.

William Osler came to be Professor of Medicine at four universities in succession – McGill, Pennsylvania, Johns Hopkins and Oxford. He left records of the autopsies performed at the Montreal General Hospital which, incidentally, are models of careful, critical observation. At the beginning of these notes, he copied out a quotation from the historian, Froude. Here it is:

> The knowledge, that a man can use, is the only real knowledge, the only knowledge which has life and growth in it, converts itself into practical power. The rest hangs like dust about the brain or dries like raindrops off the stones.

The knowledge that can be used has life and growth in it. But each man will need quick access also to much more than he is using in his own field, and the scholar who has worked faithfully through one field once knows how to find what he needs to know there. If he has kept the windows of his mind open, he makes himself doubly resourceful, for he can still communicate with those who work in other fields.

Academic honours all too often go to the student who reads narrowly and rapidly and has a detailed memory. But the man or woman with a less spectacular memory may well have a better mind and be a more effective specialist. And all men who achieve something worth while with their wits nowadays become specialists of one sort or another. Academic honours, also, often go to the precocious youth who matures first within his age group. But early precocity may reach an early plateau. The slow-starting, slow-developing Scot or Scandinavian, continuing to climb, may come abreast and pass him in the twenties with a better brain for reasoning, a clearer perspective and a capacity to make a quick exhaustive survey of pertinent facts.

Examiners in school and college may call this "cramming," as though it were unworthy of a scholar. But there is no ability of greater value in any profession than the ability to cram – to place within the focus of attention for brief review a large assortment of related facts. It makes little difference whether the field is teaching, or politics, or whether it is writing, law, medicine, the ministry or business; the use of memory alone, however excellent, can rarely replace it altogether.

What is the best way to train a specialist? Should the future scientist begin still earlier with chemistry, or physics, or biology, and restrict his attention to that? That may be the way to win some scholarships and perhaps to train a technician. But, in my opinion and experience, it is not the way to make a resourceful investigator, nor the most effective teacher, nor a good citizen. Should the scholar in the humanities ignore science? Should the business man ignore both the humanities and the sciences, and concentrate on methods of trade and on economic statistics? What of the politician, the modern farmer, the artist, the musician, the journalist? No, in almost every case a broad education in the late teens and early twenties, before the special studies, will produce a better and more resourceful specialist.

But you cannot now alter your previous preparation, or change the homes and the schools that made you what you are at present, any more than you can alter the blood that your heart is pumping, or change the germ plasma you will inevitably hand down to your descendants, if you are blessed with them. Nevertheless, you can broaden your education now. It is never too late, and it is quite simple. The vast opportunity of idleness lies before you. If you do not use it, your specializing will expose you to an insidious disease that can shut you away from all but your occupational associates. It will imprison you in lonely solitude.

You have all seen examples of what I mean. The victim, who may well be expert in some special discipline, comes home from business, or teaching, or laboratory, or farm, and finds no means of communication with wife and children. He talks his "shop" for a time and then falls silent, subsiding into stupid isolation.

If he drinks a cocktail or two, the chances of emerging from the isolation are decreased. Alcohol does have its uses, no doubt, but it has no contribution to make to the daily round of a professional man.

The victim of this isolating disease might say that he is too tired to be bothered to look into the lives of the other members of the family. That is not the truth. The truth is that he has forgotten how to open windows too long closed. He could have done it when he was younger. Idleness has lost its thrill for him. The eager child that once looked out of his eyes is still there, perhaps, but it has fallen into a deep sleep. And he is left alone, aware of hunger, no doubt, and of sexual urges, perhaps, but intellectually all alone in selfish preoccupation. The specialist who continues to think of his specialty in time off has neither rest nor recreation.

Recently C. P. Snow, the novelist, once a scientist, has described the phenomenon of "two cultures." It is most often encountered, he writes, in our universities. Those devoted to science and those in the humanities no longer communicate with each other. Their cultures separate them and they speak different languages. They are unhappy and irritated when not left to themselves. But what Sir Charles Snow is describing is only one example of a much more general phenomenon prevalent today in society. Within science itself, separate groups have formed. Each uses a technical lingo incomprehensible to other groups. Even doctors of medicine use strange genteelisms and jargon in laboratory and hospital. When they talk to patients, or write reports, they continue to use it, as though hoping to impress someone. Or else they forget the fact that simpler diction would be better suited to humane purposes and to scholarly performance. The rancher, the business man, the technologist, the musician and even the beatnik and the crook have a language of their own. As the years pass, they find general communication increasingly difficult.

All this specialization has been made necessary by the vast accumulation of facts and skills. But the insulation of the disciplines from each other is not inevitable. It can be prevented. It can even be cured if the underlying pathology is understood.

The cause of the isolation of the cultures is closure of the windows of the mind.

Do not change too much in growing up. Keep the secrets you knew as a child, the curiosity and the open mind. Learn from the child that the best rest from doing one thing is doing another until you fall into a sound sleep. It is the vigorous use of idle time that will broaden your education, make you a more efficient specialist, a happier man, a more useful citizen. It will help you to understand the rest of the world and make you more resourceful.

It may well help you to lead a balanced life if you keep a secret commonplace book, a journal, a diary – not so much to make a record of events as to note down good quotations, and to summarize your problems and argue out your own beliefs. Some would say you are listening and talking to God. Perhaps they are right. Every man, young or old, needs a confessor and a chance to state his own case in honest secrecy, and a notebook serves this purpose for an educated man quite well. When you read, re-state some of your reading in notes, in your own words. When you walk, observe the world, hear the birds, see beauty, direct your thoughts, as they go wandering off, to constructive fantasies. Such fantasies form the patterns that will determine your later behaviour.

What practical proof can I produce that broadening the base of culture will humanize the specialist? Will it really make him more effective in his specialty as well as a happier, kinder, human being? I have known a few men that I would call truly great. They were all men who had vivid interests in idle time, interests that enriched the mind and made them more resourceful in their specialties. The man of narrow training and narrow outlook may work longer hours and yet fail to see what such men saw.

Superlative achievement comes most often from the man who broadens the basis of his own culture all through life without lessening the intensity of work in his chosen field. This is how men come to balanced leadership. Here is society's hope of scientists who will guide government, and humanists who will control the power of science.

Beware, then, of the great social disease, the closure of the windows of the mind, the loneliness of selfish solitude, the isolation that limits achievement for so many specialists. Welcome the wind from the Ocean of Truth. Walk on its shores and be content to pick up the pebbles you find, listening there for the whisper of wisdom meant for every man.

Of the essays and addresses included in this book, the following made their first appearance in the publications named:

1   Published in altered form in *Perspectives in Biology and Medicine,* Vol. IV, 4, 1961.

2   *Princeton Alumni Weekly,* Vol. 37, 26, 1937.

3   *Canadian Medical Association Journal,* Vol. 85, 173, 1961.

4   *The Writer,* Vol. 74, 3, 1961.

5   *Journal of Medical Education,* Vol. 37, 90-96, 1962.

6   *University of Western Ontario Medical Journal,* Vol. 11, 79, 1941.

7   *Brain,* Vol. 80, 3, 1957.

8   *Archives of Neurology and Psychiatry,* Vol. 16, 213, 1926.

9   *Nova Scotia Medical Bulletin,* December 1953.

10   *Transactions,* College of Physicians of Philadelphia, Vol. 24, 1, 1956.

12   *Proceedings,* American Academy of Arts and Sciences, Vol. 82, Part 5, 1953.

14   *Control of the Mind,* ed. by S. M. Farber and R. J. L. Wilson. San Francisco: McGraw-Hill, 1961.

16   *Journal of Neurosurgery,* Vol. VI, 1, 6-12, 1949.

17   *Queen's Quarterly,* Vol. 64, 2, 1961.

18   *McGill News,* XLII, 1, 1961.

19   *The Medical Journal of Australia,* December 22, 1962.

      Nos. 11, 13, 15 have not been published previously.

Date Due

APR 30 '68 Hensall				
MAY 30 '68				
July 23				
Brucefield				
Cranbrook				
LAKE May 73				
FOR Aug '73